Nine Papers from the
International Congress
of Mathematicians 1986

AMERICAN MATHEMATICAL SOCIETY
TRANSLATIONS

Series 2
Volume 147

Nine Papers from the International Congress of Mathematicians 1986

by

I. G. Bashmakova A. M. Olevskiĭ

G. V. Belyĭ M. G. Peretyat'kin

E. D. Gluskin A. A. Razborov

S. K. Godunov A. V. Skorokhod

A. A. Gonchar

AMERICAN MATHEMATICAL SOCIETY
PROVIDENCE, RHODE ISLAND

Translation edited by BEN SILVER

1980 *Mathematics Subject Classification* (1985 *Revision*). Primary 03C57, 11-03, 11D09, 11R32, 30E10, 42-02, 42A20, 42A24, 42A28, 42A61, 42C10, 46-02, 46B20, 60-02, 60B99, 60G07, 65F15, 68Q15, 94C10; Secondary 11D25, 11D41, 20E05, 20E07, 20E18, 42C20, 43A46, 46B15, 60G42.

International Congress of Mathematicians (1986: Berkeley, Calif.)
  Nine papers from the International Congress of Mathematicians 1986 / by I. G. Bash-makova ... [et al.; translation edited by Ben Silver].
  p. cm. – (American Mathematical Society translations, ISSN 0065-9290; ser. 2, v. 147)
  Translated from the Russian.
  Includes bibliographical references.
  ISBN 0-8218-3133-X (alk. paper)
  1. Mathematics–Congresses. I. Bashmakova, I. G. (Izabella Grigor'evna) II. Silver, Ben. III. Title. IV. Title: 9 papers from the International Congress of Mathematicians 1986. V. Series.
QA3.A572 ser. 2, vol. 147
[QA1]
510 s–dc20   90-22430
[510]   CIP

This publication was typeset using $\mathcal{A}_\mathcal{M}\mathcal{S}$-TEX,
the American Mathematical Society's TEX macro system.

10 9 8 7 6 5 4 3 2 1   94 93 92 91 90

Contents

Russian Contents*

---

*The American Mathematical Society scheme for transliteration of Cyrillic may be found
at the end of index issues of *Mathematical Reviews.*

Amer. Math. Soc. Transl.
(2) Vol. **147**, 1990

Random Processes in Infinite-Dimensional Spaces

A. V. SKOROKHOD

In recent years more and more attention in the theory of random processes has been devoted to the study of random processes in infinite-dimensional spaces. The interest in such processes is due not only to the desire to extend the known methods of investigation of finite-dimensional processes, but also to the fact that infinite-dimensional processes arise also in the solution of many problems that are natural for finite-dimensional processes. The peculiarities and difficulties that arise in the consideration of infinite-dimensional processes are connected first and foremost with the geometric structure of the space. Therefore, such difficulties disappear if it is possible to find a suitable mapping of the original space into some other space. We remark that these difficulties appear in the consideration of questions on a constructive plane (the study of properties of sample functions, the investigation of convergence of random processes, the construction of stochastic integrals, and the definition and investigation of solutions of stochastic differential equations). General measure theory questions are indifferent to the topology.

In this paper we digress from the topology of the phase space and investigate a random process in a measurable space with a countably generated σ-algebra. Such spaces form a sufficiently broad class, and only such spaces can be used in applications. The structure of the measurable process is cleared up. Certain invariants of the process are defined which under very broad restrictions determine the process to within nonanticipative invertible transformations. Among these invariants is the rank of the process, which can be equal either to $+\infty$ or to a positive integer. The rank is the essential dimension of the process. A random time change and a nonanticipative transformation can be used to reduce the process to a process in R^∞ sat-

1980 *Mathematics Subject Classification* (1985 *Revision*). Primary 60-02, 60G07; Secondary 60G42.

Translation of Proc. Internat. Congr. Math. (Berkeley, Calif., 1986), Vol. 1, Amer. Math. Soc., Providence, R. I., 1987, pp. 163–171; MR **89e**:60081.

isfying a linear stochastic differential equation of Itô type. The rank of the process is the number of independent Wiener processes in the equation.

Results of Meyer, Kunita, Watanabe, and Dellacherie on martingale theory and the general theory of random processes will be used below without special references. These results are widely known and occur in the books of these authors and in many other books on the theory of random processes.

1. The theorem of Kolmogorov

A random process is defined to be a triple composed of the following objects: !) a probability space $(\Omega, \mathscr{F}, P)$; 2) a phase space $(X, \mathscr{B})$, which is a measurable space; and 3) a mapping $x(t, \omega) : R_+ \times \Omega \to X$ having the property that for all $t \in R_+$ the mapping $x(t, \cdot) : \Omega \to X$ is measurable with respect to the σ-algebras $\mathscr{F}$ and $\mathscr{B}$. The function $x(t, \omega)$ is a random process in the phase space X, defined on the nonnegative half-line R_+. The probability space plays an essential role only in the case when the process is defined with the help of some construction. In the general treatment of random processes the finite-dimensional distributions constitute the main characteristic of a process. This is the family of functions

$$\mu_{t_1, \ldots, t_n}(B_1, \ldots, B_n) = P\{x(t_1, \omega) \in B_1, \ldots, x(t_n, \omega) \in B_n\},$$

$$n = 1, 2, \ldots, \quad t_k \in R_+, \quad B_k \in \mathscr{B}. \quad (1)$$

These functions satisfy the following consistency conditions:

1) $\mu_{t_{i_1}, \ldots, t_{i_n}}(B_{i_1}, \ldots, B_{i_n}) = \mu_{t_1, \ldots, t_n}(B_1, \ldots, B_n)$, where $\{i_1, \ldots, i_n\} = \{1, 2, \ldots, n\}$, $n = 1, 2, \ldots$, $t_k \in R_+$, and $B_k \in \mathscr{B}$.

2) $\mu_{t_1, \ldots, t_{n-1}, t_n}(B_1, \ldots, B_{n-1}, X) = \mu_{t_1, \ldots, t_{n-1}}(B_1, \ldots, B_{n-1})$.

3) $\mu_{t_1, \ldots, t_n}(B, B_2, \ldots, B_n)$ is a measure with respect to B, $\mu_t(X) = 1$.

The Kolmogorov theorem asserts that for every collection of consistent finite-dimensional distributions there is a random process $x(t, \omega)$ on some probability space $\{\Omega, \mathscr{F}, P\}$ such that (1) holds.

As Ω one can take the space X^{R_+} of all X-valued functions on R_+; $\mathscr{F}$ will be the cylindrical σ-algebra in X^{R_+}, and the measure P is uniquely determined by the finite-dimensional distributions by

$$P(\{x(\cdot) : x(t_1) \in B_1, \ldots, x(t_n) \in B_n\}) = \mu_{t_1, \ldots, t_n}(B_1, \ldots, B_n).$$

The process $x(t, \omega)$ itself is given by the relation

$$x(t, \omega(\cdot)) = \omega(t), \quad \omega(\cdot) \in X^{R_+}.$$

2. Measurability

Let $x(t, \omega)$ and $\tilde{x}(t, \omega)$ be two random processes on the same probability space. They are said to be *stochastically equivalent* if for all $t \in R_+$

$$P\{x(t, \omega) = \tilde{x}(t, \omega)\} = 1.$$

In this case $x(t, \omega)$ and $\tilde{x}(t, \omega)$ are said to be *modifications* of each other. In specifying a process by finite-dimensional distributions it is natural not to distinguish between modifications. Further study of a random process also does not depend on the choice of modification.

A process is said to be *measurable* if it has a measurable modification, i.e., a modification $\tilde{x}(t, \omega)$ that is a measurable mapping of the space $(R_+ \times \Omega, \mathscr{B}_{R_+} \otimes \mathscr{F})$ into $(X, \mathscr{B})$, where $\mathscr{B}_{R_+}$ is the Borel σ-algebra in R_+.

For what follows we need some spaces of random variables. Denote by $R(\Omega)$ the space of all numerical variables on the probability space $\{\Omega, \mathscr{F}, P\}$. If $\xi, \eta \in R(\Omega)$, then

$$\rho(\xi, \eta) = \mathsf{E}(1 - e^{-|\xi - \eta|})$$

is a metric in $R(\Omega)$, and $R(\Omega)$ is a complete space with respect to it.

Let H_t be the closure in this metric of the set of variables of the form $g(x(s_1, \omega), \ldots, x(s_n, \omega))$, where $n = 1, 2, \ldots,$ $s_k \in R_+,$ $s_k \le t,$ and $g(x_1, \ldots, x_n)$ is a $\mathscr{B}^n$-measurable function of X^n into R.

The quantities H_t are determined by the flow of the process up through the time t.

Denote by H the closure of $\bigcup_t H_t$.

THEOREM 1. *Suppose that the σ-algebra $\mathscr{B}$ is countably generated. The process $x(t, \omega)$ is measurable if and only if* (1) H *is separable, and* (2) $\mu_{s,t}(B_1, B_2)$ *is a Borel function of s for any $t \in R_+$ and $B_1, B_2 \in \mathscr{B}$.*

In the case of a countably generated $(X, \mathscr{B})$ this space can be mapped into the interval $[0, 1]$ by a measurable one-to-one mapping. Nevertheless, this does not give a basis for asserting that, in essence, all processes with such phase spaces are one-dimensional. It will be assumed below that the σ-algebra $\mathscr{B}$ is countably generated, while the process $x(t, \omega)$ is measurable.

3. The determining flow of σ-algebras

The time evolution of a process determines how the spaces H_t change. We remark that these spaces do not change under one-to-one nonanticipative transformations of the random process, in particular, not under one-to-one mappings of the phase spaces. Instead of the family of spaces H_t we can consider the flow of σ-algebras $(\mathscr{F}_t)$, where $\mathscr{F}_t$ is the σ-algebra of events generated by the random variables in H_t. Since $\mathscr{F}_t$ and H_t determine each other, we shall study the structure of the flow $(\mathscr{F}_t)$. Denote by $\mathscr{M}_2$ the space of square-integrable $(\mathscr{F}_t)$-adapted martingales.

THEOREM 2. (1) $\mathscr{M}_2$ *determines the flow $(\mathscr{F}_t)$.*

(2) *There exists a countable set $\{\eta_n(t), n = 1, 2, \ldots\}$ of martingales in $\mathscr{M}_2$ such that the values of the martingales are dense in H_t for each $t \in R_+$.*

Below we need the following conditions on the flow $(\mathscr{F}_t)$:

(1) $\mathscr{F}$ is complete with respect to P, and $\mathscr{F}_t$ contains all the sets of measure 0.

(2) $\mathscr{F}_t = \bigcap \mathscr{F}_{t+} = \bigcap_{s>t} \mathscr{F}_s$.

Under these conditions the martingales in $\mathscr{M}_2$ have right-continuous modifications without discontinuities of the second kind. It can be assumed that $\mathscr{M}_2$ consists only of such martingales. We denote by $\mathscr{W}$ and $\mathscr{P}$ the σ-algebras of well-measurable and predictable sets in $R_+ \times \Omega$. The first is generated by the right-continuous adapted processes, and the second by the continuous adapted processes.

For $\eta_1(t)$ and $\eta_2(t)$ in $\mathscr{M}_2$ we denote by $\langle \eta_1, \eta_2 \rangle_t$ their reciprocal characteristic—the $\mathscr{P}$-measurable process such that $\eta_1(t)\eta_2(t) - \langle \eta_1, \eta_2 \rangle_t$ is a martingale. The variable $\langle \eta, \eta \rangle_t = \langle \eta \rangle_t$ is the characteristic of the martingale $\eta(t)$. Two martingales $\eta_1(t)$ and $\eta_2(t)$ in $\mathscr{M}_2$ are *orthogonal* $(\eta_1 \perp \eta_2)$ if $\langle \eta_1, \eta_2 \rangle_t = 0$ for all $t \in R_+$.

THEOREM 3. $\mathscr{M}_2 = \mathscr{M}_2^0 \oplus \mathscr{M}_2^1 \oplus \mathscr{M}_2^2$ (*orthogonal sum in the sense of the orthogonality concept introduced*), *where* $\mathscr{M}_2^0$ *is the space of continuous martingales,* $\mathscr{M}_2^1$ *is the space of purely discontinuous compensated martingales with continuous characteristics, and* $\mathscr{M}_2^2$ *is the space of purely discontinuous martingales with purely discontinuous characteristics.*

This decomposition has an analogue in the well-known Lévy decomposition of a process with independent increments into a purely discontinuous component $(\mathscr{M}_2^2)$, a stochastically continuous jump component $(\mathscr{M}_2^1)$, and a continuous component. As we shall see later, this analogy can be extended deeper.

4. The essential time. The rank

Let us consider the space $\mathscr{M}_2^0 \oplus \mathscr{M}_2^1$ of all martingales in $\mathscr{M}_2$ with continuous characteristics. By choosing some dense sequence of martingales in $\mathscr{M}_2^0 \oplus \mathscr{M}_2^1$ and considering their characteristics we can construct a martingale $\overline{\eta}(t) \in \mathscr{M}_2^0 \oplus \mathscr{M}_2^1$ such that for every other martingale $\eta(t) \in \mathscr{M}_2^0 \oplus \mathscr{M}_2^1$ the increasing function $\langle \eta \rangle_t$ is absolutely continuous with respect to the increasing function $\langle \overline{\eta} \rangle_t = \delta_t$. Every such function δ_t (it is representable as the characteristic of some martingale, and the characteristics of all other martingales in $\mathscr{M}_2^0 \oplus \mathscr{M}_2^1$ are absolutely continuous with respect to it) will be called an *essential time* for the flow $(\mathscr{F}_t)$ (or for the original process). If δ_t is not increasing on some interval, then on this interval the original process evolves deterministically, although the evolution depends on what happened before this interval of time. It is obvious that an essential time is determined to within equivalence: if δ_t is an essential time and $\hat{\delta}_t$ is a continuous increasing adapted process for which

$$P\{0 < d\hat{\delta}_t/d\delta_t < \infty\} = 1,$$

then $\hat{\delta}_t$ is also an essential time.

We now consider the space $\mathcal{M}_2^0$. Suppose that $\{\eta_n(t)\}$ is dense in $\mathcal{M}_2^0$. We orthogonalize $\{\eta_n(t)\}$ as follows:

$$\xi_1(t) = \eta_1(t), \qquad \xi_r(t) = \eta_n(t) - \sum_{k=1}^{n-1} \int_0^t \alpha_{nk}(s)\, d\xi_k(s), \quad n > 1,$$

$$\alpha_{nk}(s) = \frac{d\langle \eta_n, \xi_k \rangle}{d\langle \xi_k \rangle_s}.$$

The sequence $\{\xi_k(t)\}$ has the following property: each martingale $\eta(t) \in \mathcal{M}_2^0$ can be represented in the form

$$\eta(t) = \sum_{k=1}^{\infty} \int_0^t \alpha_k(s)\, d\xi_k(s), \qquad \alpha_k(s) = \frac{d\langle \eta, \xi_k \rangle_s}{d\langle \xi_k \rangle_s}.$$

Every sequence with this property will be called a *basis* in $\mathcal{M}_2^0$.

THEOREM 4. *Suppose that* $\delta(t)$ *is an essential time, and* $\{\xi_k(t)\}$ *and* $\{\tilde{\xi}_k(t)\}$ *are two bases in* $\mathcal{M}_2^0$. *In this case, if*

$$\nu(t) = \sum_k I_{\{d\langle \xi_k \rangle_t / d\delta(t) > 0\}}, \qquad \tilde{\nu}(t) = \sum_k I_{\{d\langle \tilde{\xi}_k \rangle_t / d\delta(t) > 0\}},$$

then

$$P\left\{ \int I_{\{\nu(s) \neq \tilde{\nu}(s)\}}\, d\delta(s) = 0 \right\} = 1.$$

Thus, there exists a $\mathscr{P}$-measurable function $r(t)$ independent of the choice of basis such that $P\{\nu(t) = r(t)\} = 1$, and $r(t)$ is called the *rank* of the flow $(\mathscr{F}_t)$ at the time t. The quantity

$$r = \inf\left\{ k : P\left\{ \int I_{\{\nu(s) > k\}}\, d\delta(s) = 0 \right\} = 1 \right\}$$

($\inf \varnothing$ is regarded as $+\infty$) is called the rank of the *flow* $(\mathscr{F}_t)$. The rank of a flow is the dimension of a minimal basis in $\mathcal{M}_2^0$, as follows from the next statement.

THEOREM 5. *Suppose that* $\delta(t)$ *is an essential time, and* r *is the rank of* $(\mathscr{F}_t)$. *There exists a sequence of* $\mathscr{P}$-*measurable sets* $A_1 \supset A_2 \supset \cdots \supset A_r$ (*this sequence is infinite for* $r = +\infty$) *and a basis* $\{\xi_k(t), \ k < r + 1\}$ *such that*

$$\langle \xi_i \rangle_t = \int_0^t I_{A_i}(s)\, d\delta(s).$$

5. Examples

The martingales in $\mathcal{M}_2^1 \oplus \mathcal{M}_2^2$ have a fairly simple structure, although we indicate a certain determining invariant for $\mathcal{M}_2^1$ below. Here our goal is to show that a process can have various ranks, and it can be a fairly regular process in R.

EXAMPLE 1. Suppose that $x(t, \omega)$ is a process in R^m whose components $x_1(t, \omega), \dots, x_m(t, \omega)$ are independent Wiener processes. We show that its rank is $r = m$. Every martingale adapted to the flow $(\mathcal{F}_t)$ generated by $x(t, \omega)$ has the representation

$$\eta(t) = \sum_{k=1}^{m} \int_0^t \varphi_k(s)\, dx_k(s, \omega);$$

therefore, $r \le m$. If there existed a basis of $r < m$ martingales $\eta_1(t), \dots, \eta_r(t)$ and

$$x_k(t, \omega) = \sum_{i=1}^{k} \int_0^t \alpha_{ki}(s)\, d\eta_i(s),$$

then[*]

$$\delta_{lk} t = \sum_{i=1}^{r} \int_0^t \alpha_{ki}(s)^{\alpha_{kj}}\, d\langle \eta_i \rangle_s, \qquad \delta_{lk} = \sum_{i=1}^{r} \alpha_{li}\alpha_{ki}(t)\frac{d\langle \eta_i \rangle_t}{dt},$$

$l, k \le m$, which is impossible (the rank of the matrix $\|\alpha_{ki}(d\langle \eta_i \rangle/ds)^{1/2}\|$ does not exceed $r \le m$).

EXAMPLE 2. Let $\{w_k(t)\}$ be a sequence of independent Wiener processes, and define

$$\eta_{n, n+1}(t) = \int_0^t (\arctan w_{n+1}(s) + \pi/2)\, dw_n(s),$$

$$\eta_{n, m}(t) = \int_0^t (\arctan \eta_{n+1, m}(s) + \pi/2)\, dw_n(s), \qquad m > n + 1.$$

The flow $(\mathcal{F}_t^{n, m})$ generated by the martingale $\eta_{n, m}(t)$ coincides with the flow generated by the Wiener processes $w_n(t), w_{n+1}(t), \dots, w_m(t)$, and its rank is equal to $m - n + 1$. It is easy to see that the limit $\lim_{m \to \infty} \eta_{n, m}(t) = \eta_n(t)$ exists in mean-square convergence, and the flow $\mathcal{F}_t^n$ generated by the limit process coincides with the flow generated by the Wiener processes $w_n(t), w_{n+1}(t), \dots$. It has rank $+\infty$. At the same time, the processes $\eta_{n, m}(t)$ and $\eta_n(t)$ are one-dimensional continuous martingales with differentiable characteristics.

6. Quasicontinuous flows $(\mathcal{F}_t)$. Random time change

A flow is said to be *quasicontinuous* if $\mathcal{M}_2^2$ contains the point 0. In this case, the characteristics of all the martingales in $\mathcal{M}_2$ are continuous. Let $\delta(t)$ be an essential time, and suppose that $\delta(t) \uparrow +\infty$ as $t \uparrow +\infty$. Let $\tau_t = \delta^{-1}(t)$, $\tilde{x}(t, \omega) = x(\tau_t, \omega)$, and $(\tilde{\mathcal{F}}_t) = (\mathcal{F}_{\tau_t})$, and let $\tilde{\mathcal{M}}_2$, $\tilde{\mathcal{M}}_2^0$, $\tilde{\mathcal{M}}_2^1$, and $\tilde{\mathcal{M}}_2^2$ correspond to the flow $(\tilde{\mathcal{F}}_t)$.

---

[*] Editor's note. The formulas for $\delta_{lk} t$ and δ_{lk} are reproduced here as they appear in the original, but there are apparently misprints.

THEOREM 6. $\tilde{\mathcal{M}}_2 = \{\eta(\tau_t), \eta \in \mathcal{M}_2\}$ and $\tilde{\mathcal{M}}_2^i = \{\eta(\tau_t), \eta \in \mathcal{M}_2^i\}$, $i = 0, 1, 2$. The process $\tilde{x}(t, \omega)$ does not necessarily generate $(\tilde{\mathcal{F}}_t)$; it can be nonrandom in general.

A flow is said to be *absolutely continuous* if it is continuous and an essential time is absolutely continuous (differentiable with respect to t). The time change given above leads to the condition that the flow $(\tilde{\mathcal{F}}_t)$ is absolutely continuous.

THEOREM 7. Let $(\mathcal{F}_t)$ be an absolutely continuous flow.

1) There exists a sequence $\{w_k(t)\}$ of Wiener processes and a Poisson measure $\pi(dx \times dt)$ on R_+^2 with $E\pi(ds \times dx) = dx\, dt$ such that every martingale $\eta(t) \in \mathcal{M}_2$ is representable in the form

$$\eta(t) = \sum_{k=1}^{\infty} \int_0^t \alpha_k(s)\, dw_k(s) + \int_0^t \int_{R_+} \gamma(s, x)[\pi(ds \times dx) - ds\, dx], \qquad (2)$$

where $\alpha_k(s)$ and $\gamma(s, x)$ are functions measurable with respect to $\mathcal{P}$ and $\mathcal{P} \otimes \mathcal{B}_{R_+}$, respectively, such that for all $t > 0$

$$P\left\{ \sum \int_0^t \alpha_k^2(s)\, ds + \int_0^t \int_{R_+} \gamma^2(s, x)\, ds\, dx < \infty \right\} = 1.$$

2) There exist $\mathcal{P}$-measurable functions $r(t)$ and $\lambda(t)$, the first taking the values $0, 1, \ldots, +\infty$ and the second taking values in R_+ or $+\infty$, such that $\mathcal{F}_t$ coincides with the flow generated by the processes

$$\left\{ \int_0^t I_{\{r(s) \geq k\}}\, dw_k(s), \ k = 1, 2, \ldots ; \ \int_0^t \int_{R_+} I_{\{x \leq \lambda(t)\}} \frac{1}{1 + x^2} \pi(ds \times dx) \right\},$$

and $r(t)$ is the rank of the flow. The function $\lambda(t)$ has the following meaning. For $s < t$ let $\nu(t) - \nu(s)$ be the number of jumps of all the martingales in $\mathcal{M}_2^1$ on $[s, t]$. Then $\int_s^t \lambda(u)\, du$ is the compensator of $\nu(t) - \nu(s)$; $\lambda(t)$ is called the width of the Poisson spectrum of $(\mathcal{F}_t)$. This quantity is also invariant under transformations of the process that preserve the flow.

7. Nonanticipative transformations and stochastic equations

Let $\{\eta_n(t)\}$ be a sequence of martingales in $\mathcal{M}_2$ such that for all t the linear span of the variables $\{\eta_n(t), n \geq 1\}$ is dense in H_t. It will be assumed that the flow is absolutely continuous. Then for each martingale $\eta_n(t)$ we can write formula (2) with the functions $\alpha_{nk}(s)$ and $\gamma_n(s, x)$. For fixed x these are $\mathcal{F}_s$-measurable random variables in H_s. Hence, they can be expressed as certain linear functions of $\{\eta_n(s), n = 1, 2, \ldots\}$. What is more, since they are predictable, and the predictable projection of $\eta_n(s)$ is $\eta_n(s-)$, they can be regarded as linear functions of $\eta_n(s-)$. We write these linear functions formally as infinite linear combinations. (In fact, they are limits of finite linear combinations.) If

$$\alpha_{nk}(s) = \sum a_{km}^n(s)\eta_m(s-),$$

$$\gamma_n(s) = \sum g_m^n(s, x)\eta_m(s-)$$

(the functions $a_{km}^n(s)$ and $g_m^n(s, x)$ are nonrandom), then for the sequence $\{\eta_n(t)\}$ we get the system of linear stochastic differential equations

$$d\eta_n(t) = \sum_{k=1}^{\infty} \left(\sum_{m=1}^{\infty} a_{km}^r(s)\eta_m(s-) \right) dw_k(s)$$

$$+ \int_{R_+} \sum_{m=1}^{\infty} g_m(s, x)\eta_m(s-)[\pi(ds \times dx) - ds\, dx]. \qquad (3)$$

This equation can be regarded as a linear equation in R^∞ with unbounded operator coefficients. Giving a precise meaning to equations (3) and investigating their solutions (in particular, uniqueness conditions) is a problem in the theory of linear stochastic differential equations.

Since the process $\eta_n(t)$ is $\mathscr{F}_t$-measurable, and $\mathscr{F}_t$ is generated by the values of the process $x(s, \omega)$ for $s \leq t$, there exists a $\mathscr{B}_{R_+} \otimes \mathscr{B}^{R_+}$-measurable function $f_n(t, x(\cdot))$ in $R_+ \times X^{R_+}$ into R such that

$$\eta_n(t) = f_n(t, x(\cdot, \omega)),$$

and the function f_n is nonanticipative: if $y_1(s) + y_2(s)$ for $s \leq t$ and $y_i(\cdot) \in X^{R_+}$, then $f_n(t, y_1(\cdot)) = f_n(t, y_2(\cdot))$. The mapping $x(t, \omega) \to \{f_n(t, x(\cdot, \omega)), n = 1, 2, \dots\}$ of the process into R^∞ preserves the flow $(\mathscr{F}_t)$, and hence it is invertible in the generalized sense. This is the invertible nonanticipative transformation into R^∞ that, after a random time change, carries a quasicontinuous process into a process satisfying the system of linear stochastic differential equations.

8. Some conclusions and problems

1. The structure of a quasicontinuous flow is completely clear. It is determined by the following three characteristics: (a) an essential time $\delta(t)$ that is determined to within equivalence for measures generated by increasing continuous functions; (b) the rank $r(t)$ of the process, which is uniquely determined almost everywhere with respect to the essential time; and (c) the width $\lambda(t)$ of the Poisson spectrum, which is uniquely determined almost everywhere with respect to the essential time if this time is fixed.

We remark that the functions $r(t)$ and $\lambda(t)$ determining the flow for $\delta(t) = t$ must be predictable with respect to the flow determined. This imposes on them definite restrictions that should be studied.

2. The special role of linear stochastic differential equations with unbounded operator coefficients has become clear. Such equations have been

studied in the framework of the theory of linear systems under very stringent restrictions; it makes sense to consider such systems without any restrictions.

3. Only certain transformations of processes and flows of σ-algebras have been considered. The question of noninvertible transformations of processes (for example, with the help of transformations of phase space) under which flows of σ-algebras are preserved is very interesting.

4. It would be useful to have a method for proving quasicontinuity of the flow generated by a random process without considering a martingale space, but instead using only its finite-dimensional distributions. (This is possible, for example, for Markov processes.)

5. The study of general flows (with predictable discontinuities) is of interest. Here the operation of taking the limit could be used for flows with finitely many predictable discontinuities.

BIBLIOGRAPHY

1. A. V. Skorokhod, *On the local structure of continuous Markov processes*, Teor. Veroyatnost. i Primenen. **11** (1966), 381–423; English transl. in Theory Probab. Appl. **11** (1966).

2. ____, *Operator stochastic differential equations and stochastic semigroups*, Uspekhi Mat. Nauk **37** (1982), no. 6(228), 157–183; English transl. in Russian Math. Surveys **37** (1982).

3. I. I. Gikhman and A. V. Skorokhod, *Stochastic differential equations and their applications*, "Naukova Dumka", Kiev, 1982. (Russian)

4. A. V. Skorokhod, *Stochastic equations for complex systems*, "Nauka", Moscow, 1983; English transl., Reidel, 1987.

Institute of Mathematics
Academy of Sciences of the Ukrainian SSR
Kiev
USSR

Translated by H. H. McFADEN

Amer. Math. Soc. Transl.
(2) Vol. **147**, 1990

Finitely Axiomatizable Theories

M. G. PERETYAT'KIN

In the author's papers [7] and [8] two constructions are described which allow one to construct finitely axiomatizable theories with various properties of algorithmic character. Besides the existence theorem, estimates of the complexity of various natural classes of sentences were obtained in these papers. The second construction, based upon the theory in [6], has a considerably larger domain of applicability, whereas the first one is simpler. In this lecture we list a series of results on finitely axiomatizable theories, extending and complementing the contents of [7] and [8].

Preliminary considerations. All theories are considered in first-order predicate logic with equality. The general notions used in this paper are to be found in the monographs of Chang and Keisler [4], Rogers [9], and Ershov [3]. A language will be called *rich* if it contains a predicate symbol of parity two or greater. Unless otherwise specified, all results are supposed to refer to an arbitrary finite rich language.

A *numeration* of a model $\mathfrak{M}$ is a mapping $\nu: N \overset{\text{onto}}{\to} |\mathfrak{M}|$. A model $\mathfrak{M}$ together with a numeration ν is called a *numerated model* and is denoted by $(\mathfrak{M}, \nu)$. A numerated model $(\mathfrak{M}, \nu)$ is called *constructive* if all its predicates and functions are recursive with respect to the numeration ν, and is called *strongly constructive* if $\text{Th}(\mathfrak{M}_\nu)$ is decidable, where $\mathfrak{M}_\nu$ is obtained by enriching the language of $\mathfrak{M}$ by a countable set of new constants c_i, $i < \omega$, and interpreting each c_i by the element $\nu(i)$. The model $\mathfrak{M}$ is called *autostable* if for any two strong constructivizations ν_1 and ν_2 of $\mathfrak{M}$, there exists a recursive isomorphism $\mu: (\mathfrak{M}, \nu_1) \to (\mathfrak{M}, \nu_2)$. Nurtazin [5] showed that if a complete decidable theory T has a strongly constructivizable simple model $\mathfrak{M}$, then $\mathfrak{M}$ is autostable if and only if the set of atoms of the Lindenbaum algebra of T is recursive.

1980 *Mathematics Subject Classification* (1985 *Revision*). Primary 03C57.

Translation of Proc. Internat. Congr. Math. (Berkeley, Calif., 1986), Vol. 1, Amer. Math. Soc., Providence, R.I., 1987, pp. 322–330; MR **89g**: 03051.

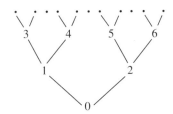

A complete binary tree is a partially ordered set $\mathscr{D}_0 = \langle N ; \preceq \rangle$ of the form represented in the picture. There are two natural operations, taking the left and the right successor, which are given by the formulas $L(x) = 2x + 1$ and $R(x) = 2x + 2$. A *tree* is any set $\mathscr{D} \subseteq N$ satisfying the following two conditions:

1. $m \preceq n$ and $n \in \mathscr{D} \to m \in \mathscr{D}$,
2. $L(n) \in \mathscr{D} \leftrightarrow R(n) \in \mathscr{D}$ for all $n \in N$.

One defines naturally the notions of dead-end of a tree, chain, maximal chain of a tree, and isolated chain in a given family of chains. $\Pi(\mathscr{D})$ will denote the family of all maximal chains of the tree $\mathscr{D}$, and $\Pi^{\mathrm{fin}}(\mathscr{D})$ the family of all finite maximal chains of $\mathscr{D}$. A tree is called *atomic* if above each of its elements lies at least one dead-end. The tree is called *superatomic* if $\Pi(\mathscr{D})$ is at most countable. By $\Pi_\alpha(\mathscr{D})$ we denote the αth iteration of the operation of discarding the isolated chains starting with $\Pi(\mathscr{D})$. From this one naturally gets the definitions of rank of a chain and rank of a tree. One can prove that the tree is superatomic if and only if $\Pi_\alpha(\mathscr{D}) = \varnothing$ for each α, i.e., all chains in $\Pi(\mathscr{D})$ have a rank. A more detailed exposition of the above notions connected with trees is given in [8].

W_s, $s < \omega$, is the Post numeration of all recursively enumerable sets, and W_s^A, $s < \omega$, is the numeration of the sets recursively enumerable with respect to the set $A \subseteq N$. By $[B]_{\mathscr{D}}$ we denote the closure of the set $B \subseteq N$ up to a tree.

We shall use the notations:

$$\mathscr{D}_s = [W_s]_{\mathscr{D}}, \quad s < \omega, \qquad \mathscr{D}_s^A = [W_s^A]_{\mathscr{D}}, \quad s < \omega, \ A \subseteq N.$$

By ε_k, $k < \omega$, we denote the truth-table conditions asserting that "the set contains the element k". By a *truth-table condition* (*tt-condition*) we shall mean a propositional formula built from elementary expressions ε_k. The statement that a truth-table condition is true in the set A will be symbolically written as $A \models \tau$. We shall denote by τ_k, $k < \omega$, a fixed Gödel numeration of all truth-table conditions. Here is another special definition:

$$\mathfrak{R}_m = \{A \subseteq N | (\forall k \in W_m) A \models \tau_k\}, \qquad m < \omega.$$

The following general theorem is a strengthening of Theorem 9.1 in [8] by the additional assertion of the autostability of the simple model.

THEOREM 1 (Main Theorem). *Let $\mathfrak{L}$ be an arbitrary finite rich language. One can construct effectively for $\mathfrak{L}$ and for a given pair of natural numbers $\langle m, s \rangle$ a finitely axiomatizable model-complete theory $F(m, s)$ in the language $\mathfrak{L}$ and a recursive sequence Ψ_n, $n \in N$, of sentences in $\mathfrak{L}$ with the following properties:*

1. The sentences Ψ_n, $n \in N$, generate the Lindenbaum algebra of $F(m, s)$.

2. The theory

$$F(m, s)[A] = F(m, s) \cup \{\Psi_i | i \in A\} \cup \{\neg\Psi_j | j \in N\backslash A\}, \qquad A \subseteq N,$$

is consistent if and only if $A \in \mathfrak{R}_m$.

3. For any $A \in \mathfrak{R}_m$ the following hold.

(a) The theory $F(m, s)[A]$ has a simple model $\leftrightarrow$ the tree $\mathscr{D}_s^A$ is atomic.

(b) The simple model of the theory $F(m, s)[A]$, if it exists, is strongly constructivizable $\leftrightarrow$ the set A is recursive and the family $\Pi^{\text{fin}}(\mathscr{D}_s^A)$ is computable.

(c) The simple model of the theory $F(m, s)[A]$, if it exists and is strongly constructivizable, is autostable with respect to the strong constructivizations $\leftrightarrow$ the tree $\mathscr{D}_s^A$ is recursive.

(d) The theory $F(m, s)[A]$ has a countable saturated model $\leftrightarrow$ the tree $\mathscr{D}_s^A$ is superatomic.

(e) The countable saturated model of the theory $F(m, s)[A]$ is strongly constructivizable $\leftrightarrow$ the set A is recursive and the family $\Pi(\mathscr{D}_s^A)$ is computable.

(f) The theory $F(m, s)[A]$ is ω-stable $\leftrightarrow$ the tree $\mathscr{D}_s^A$ is superatomic.

(g) The Morley rank of the theory $F(m, s)[A]$ is equal to

$$\max\{33, 1 + \text{Rank}\,\mathscr{D}_s^A + \gamma\},$$

where $\gamma = 2$ if the tree $\mathscr{D}_s^A$ is superatomic and $\gamma = 0$ otherwise.

PROOF. Keeping the notation in [8], we prove (c).

Let A and $\mathscr{D}_s^A$ be recursive and let $(\mathfrak{M}, \nu)$, $(\mathfrak{M}_1, \nu_1)$ be two strongly constructive simple models of the theory $F(m, s)[A]$. The existence of an effective correspondence between the frames of these models is obvious. Hence everything reduces to finding a recursive isomorphism on the set W. Since the model is simple, any element $a \in W \cap U$ generates a component which defines a K-path corresponding to some dead-end of the tree $\mathscr{D}_s^A$. The passage from a to the indicated dead-end is obviously effective. This lets us construct the recursive isomorphism of the given numerated models.

Conversely, if A is recursive but $\mathscr{D}_s^A$ is not, then the set of atomic formulas of the theory $F(m, s)[A]$ with one free variable cannot be recursive. Then by the criterion in [5] the prime model of this theory is not autostable with respect to the strong constructivizations. $\square$

Theorem 1 easily yields another general theorem on complete theories:

THEOREM 2 ($\mathscr{D}$-variant of the main theorem). *Let $\mathfrak{L}$ be a finite rich language and $\mathscr{D}$ a recursively enumerable tree. One can construct effectively with respect to $\mathfrak{L}$ and the recursively enumerable index of the tree $\mathscr{D}$ a complete, model-complete, finitely axiomatizable theory $F(\mathscr{D})$ in the language $\mathfrak{L}$ having the following properties.*

(a) *The theory $F(\mathscr{D})$ has a simple model $\leftrightarrow$ the tree $\mathscr{D}$ is atomic.*

(b) *The simple model of the theory $F(\mathscr{D})$, if it exists, is strongly constructivizable $\leftrightarrow$ the family $\Pi^{\text{fin}}(\mathscr{D})$ is computable.*

(c) *The simple model of the theory $F(\mathscr{D})$, if it exists and is strongly constructivizable, is autostable with respect to the strong constructivizations $\leftrightarrow$ the tree $\mathscr{D}$ is recursive.*

(d) *The theory $F(\mathscr{D})$ has a countable saturated model $\leftrightarrow$ the tree $\mathscr{D}$ is superatomic.*

(e) *The countable saturated model of the theory $F(\mathscr{D})$ is strongly constructivizable $\leftrightarrow$ the family $\Pi(\mathscr{D})$ is computable.*

(f) *The theory $F(\mathscr{D})$ is ω-stable $\leftrightarrow$ the tree $\mathscr{D}$ is superatomic.*

(g) *The Morley rank of the theory $F(\mathscr{D})$ is equal to*

$$\max\{33,\ 1 + \operatorname{Rank}\mathscr{D}_s^A + \gamma\},$$

where $\gamma = 2$ if the tree $\mathscr{D}$ is superatomic, and $\gamma = 0$ otherwise.

PROOF. We choose and fix an m such that $\mathfrak{R}_m = \varnothing$. In the role of $F(\mathscr{D})$ one can take the theory $F(m, s)$, where s was chosen such that $\mathscr{D}_s^\varnothing = \mathscr{D}$. □

The following theorem, characterizing the Lindenbaum algebras of finitely axiomatizable theories, is equivalent to the statements proved in [7] and [8], solving the well-known problem in Hanf's paper [11]. The same result was announced by Hanf [12], but his proof was not published.

THEOREM 3. *Let $\mathfrak{L}$ be an arbitrary finite rich language. The numerated Boolean algebra $(\mathscr{B}, \nu)$ is recursively equivalent to the Lindenbaum algebra of some finitely axiomatizable theory F in the language $\mathfrak{L}$ if and only if $(\mathscr{B}, \nu)$ is a positively numerated algebra.*

PROOF. If $(\mathscr{B}, \nu)$ is recursively equivalent to the Lindenbaum algebra of some finitely axiomatizable theory, then $(\mathscr{B}, \nu)$ is obviously a positively numerated algebra. Therefore it suffices to show how to construct F for a given positively numerated Boolean algebra $(\mathfrak{B}, \nu)$.

Let us denote by $\mathfrak{B}$ the Boolean algebra whose elements are equivalence classes of truth-table conditions, with the operations induced by the propositional connectives. Obviously, $\mathfrak{B}$ is an atomless algebra, freely generated by the elementary truth-table conditions. The algebra $\mathfrak{B}$ admits a natural constructivization μ defined by the Gödel numeration of the truth-table conditions. From parts 1 and 2 of the main theorem it follows that the Lindenbaum algebra of the theory $F(m, s)$ is recursively equivalent to the quotient algebra

$$(\mathfrak{B}/\mathscr{F}_m, \mu^*) \qquad (1)$$

where $\mathscr{F}_m$ is the filter generated by the set $\{\tau_k | k \in W_m\}$ and μ^* is the numeration of the quotient algebra induced by the numeration μ. One can easily see that each recursively enumerable filter of $\mathfrak{B}$ coincides with $\mathscr{F}_m$ for some $m < \omega$. Hence we get the required statement, since every positive numeration of the Boolean algebra is representable up to isomorphism in the form (1). □

The following theorem gives some concrete information about the possibilities for Lindenbaum algebras of finitely axiomatizable theories.

THEOREM 4. *Let $\mathfrak{L}$ be an arbitrary finite rich language.*

(a) *The Lindenbaum algebra defined by the empty set of axioms of $\mathfrak{L}$ is nonconstructivizable.*

(b) *There exists a decidable finitely axiomatizable theory in $\mathfrak{L}$ with a constructivizable but not strongly constructivizable Lindenbaum algebra of any of the elementary types, except those categorical in power $\delta \leq \omega$.*

PROOF. (a) Let us denote by $\mathfrak{B}(\mathfrak{L})$ the given algebra. In [10] a nonconstructivizable positively numerated Boolean algebra is produced. By Theorem 3, there exists a finitely axiomatizable theory F of the given language having a nonconstructivizable Lindenbaum algebra. One can easily see that the Lindenbaum algebra $\mathfrak{B}(F)$ is isomorphic to a quotient algebra of $\mathfrak{B}(\mathfrak{L})$ with respect to some principal filter. From this follows the nonconstructivizability of the algebra $\mathfrak{B}(\mathfrak{L})$.

(b) In [1] one constructs a constructivizable but not strongly constructivizable Boolean algebra of any of the elementary types indicated in the theorem. The needed finitely axiomatizable theory is obtained using a theorem of [3]. □

The following theorem solves two problems from Harrington's paper [13] and also a problem from [7].

THEOREM 5. (a) *There exists a complete finitely axiomatizable ω-stable theory of finite Morley rank whose simple model and countable saturated model are not constructivizable.*

(b) *There exists a complete finitely axiomatizable ω-stable theory of finite Morley rank whose simple model is strongly constructivizable but is not autostable with respect to the strong constructivizations.*

PROOF. (a) Consider the recursively enumerable superatomic tree $\mathscr{D}$ constructed in [2], for which the families $\Pi(\mathscr{D})$ and $\Pi^{\text{fin}}(\mathscr{D})$ are not computable. By construction, the rank of the tree is finite. From the model completeness of the theory $F(\mathscr{D})$ it follows that the constructivizability of its models is equivalent with their strong constructivizability. It follows by Theorem 2 that $F(\mathscr{D})$ is the desired theory.

(b) The mentioned properties are possessed by the theory $F(\mathscr{D}')$, where $\mathscr{D}'$ is a recursively enumerable nonrecursive superatomic tree of finite rank for which the family $\Pi^{\text{fin}}(\mathscr{D}')$ is computable. $\square$

The following theorem, announced in [8], strengthens the result of Lachlan [14], proved for countable theories. Lachlan's actual construction gives a decidable theory.

THEOREM 6. *There exists a complete finitely axiomatizable theory T of Morley rank $\alpha_T = \omega_1$.*

PROOF. Here we just sketch a proof, for the understanding of which a detailed knowledge of the constructions in [7] and [8] is necessary. For the construction of T we use a new construction, for the characterization of which we shall use the terminology in [8].

The frame of T has the form of a net, built on the basis of the theory of quasisuccessors [6]. In this theory an infinite number of Turing machines operate, using the information given by a common oracle. For this, the information of the oracle has to be stored without gaps in successive cells of the one-sided infinite tape, bounded to the right by the point O. To the right of this point lies the domain of operation.

One of the machines is active with respect to the oracle. It must form its content in such a way that upon finite moves to the left of O, all possible finite combinations of successively arranged zeros and ones occur. As a result, by the compactness theorem, in the nonstandard parts of the oracle arbitrary successions of zeros and ones can be found.

All passive machines have one and the same program, but the construction of the frame of the theory T must ensure that all of them operate in different planes and take in the content of the oracle with different shifts relative to the point O. Every passive machine performs work analogous to that described in the construction in [8]. Roughly speaking, the program of a passive machine must ensure the processing, by division of the cells of the tape, of the content of the oracle A in the tree $[A]_{\mathscr{D}}$, which must be connected with the head affecting the Morley rank of the corresponding formulas. Since the content of the oracle of the passive machine may be an arbitrary set $A \subseteq N$, the corresponding tree $[A]_{\mathscr{D}}$ may be superatomic of arbitrary countable rank. As a result, in the theory T there will exist formulas with parameters, of arbitrarily large countable rank. For instance, this applies to the formulas with parameters, taken from the nonstandard parts of the oracle. Thus we obtain $\alpha_T = \omega_1$. $\square$

Now using the effectiveness of the construction of finitely axiomatizable theories, which is guaranteed by the main theorem, we study the complexity of two important classes of sentences. First, we consider the class of sentences studied by Vaught [15], where the lower bound Π_1^0 was obtained.

THEOREM 7. *Let* FA *be a class of models of a given finite rich language, having finitely axiomatizable theory. Then* $\mathrm{Th}(\mathrm{FA}) \approx \Pi_3^0$.

PROOF. The set $\mathrm{Th}(\mathrm{FA})$ is recursively isomorphic to the complement of the set $L = \{n \mid \Phi_n$ has finitely axiomatizable completion$\}$. Hence it is sufficient to prove that $L \approx \Sigma_3^0$. We have

$$n \in L \leftrightarrow (\exists \Psi)(\Phi_n \ \& \ \Psi \text{ is a complete theory}).$$

Taking into account that the property "complete theory" is described by a prefix of the form $\forall \exists$, we obtain for L the upper estimate Σ_3^0. For the lower estimate we consider the standard set $S = \{n \mid N \backslash W_n$ is finite$\}$ [9, §14.8]. The theory T_n in the language $\mathfrak{L} = \{P_0^1, P_1^1, \ldots, P_s^1, \ldots\}$, defined by the set of axioms

$$\{(\exists x)(\forall y)x = y\} \cup \{(\forall x)P_i(x), \ i \in W_m\},$$

will have a finitely axiomatizable completion iff $n \in S$. Let $f(x)$ be a general recursive function such that the sentence $\Phi_{f(n)}$ defines a finitely axiomatizable theory with Lindenbaum algebra isomorphic to the Lindenbaum algebra of the theory T_n. Then

$$n \in S \leftrightarrow \Phi_{f(n)} \text{ has a finitely axiomatizable completion.}$$

This gives the needed lower estimate for L. □

There is still another estimate of the complexity of a class of formulas.

THEOREM 8. $\{n \mid \Phi_n$ *defines a complete stable theory*$\} \approx \Pi_2^0$.

PROOF. Using the well-known result of Shelah about the characterization of stable theories [4, 7.1.33], we obtain that n belongs to the set considered in the theorem if and only if Φ_n defines a complete theory that does not have the properties of a linear order. Each of these conditions is described by a prefix of the form $\forall \exists$. For the lower estimate we take the standard Π_2^0-set $I = \{n \mid W_n$ is infinite$\}$, defined in [9, §14.8]. Consider the language $\mathfrak{L}'$, containing only the equality predicate. By Δ_k we denote the sentence stating that there exist at least k different elements. Consider the theory T_n in the language $\mathfrak{L}'$, defined by the set of axioms $\{\Delta_k \mid k \in W_n\}$. It is easy to see that this theory is complete if and only if $n \in I$. One can construct effectively with respect to n a finitely axiomatizable theory F such that $\mathfrak{B}(T_n) \approx \mathfrak{B}(F)$. Let $\Phi_{f(n)}$ be the axiom for the theory F. By construction $n \in I \to \Phi_{f(n)}$ is complete, while $n \notin I \to \Phi_{f(n)}$ is not complete. As remarked in [8], the theory $\Phi_{f(n)}$ will always be superstable when it is complete. In particular it will be stable. Hence $n \in I \to \Phi_{f(n)}$ is complete and stable, while $n \notin I \to \Phi_{f(n)}$ is not complete. This gives the necessary lower estimate. □

In conclusion we discuss an open problem naturally arising in connection with the above results on finitely axiomatizable theories. For this we need some definitions.

An interpretation I of the theory T in the theory F will be called *proper* if the following conditions are satisfied:

1. $\vdash_T \varphi \leftrightarrow \vdash_F \varphi^{(I)}$;

2. the set $\{\varphi^{(I)} | \varphi$ a sentence of the theory $T\}$ generates the Lindenbaum algebra of the theory F;

3. $\varphi^{(I)}$ can be found uniformly from φ.

Let C be a property that may be possessed by a complete theory, and let I be an interpretation of the theory T in the theory F satisfying conditions 1 and 2. We say that I *preserves property* C if for any completion T^* of T the corresponding completion F^* of F, defined by I, has property C if and only if T^* does.

Let us denote by K^* the class of models of the language

$$\mathfrak{L}^* = \{P_0^1, P_1^1, \ldots, P_n^1, \ldots, n \in N\}$$

in which there are no finite definable sets. The following result is essentially a reformulation of Theorem 1 in terms of interpretations.

THEOREM 9. *Every recursively axiomatizable theory T in the language $\mathfrak{L}^*$ with the property $\operatorname{Mod} T \subseteq K^*$ can be properly interpreted in some finitely axiomatizable model-complete theory in a given finite rich language $\mathfrak{L}$ with the preservation of the following properties:*

1. *ω-stability;*

2. *the existence of a simple model, its constructivizability, and its autostability; and*

3. *the existence of a countable saturated model and its strong constructivizability.*

It is natural to ask whether similar statements are true without restrictions on the theory and with a larger list of properties. In this way we arrive at what seems to me a highly plausible conjecture about the expressive power of finitely axiomatizable theories.

CONJECTURE. Every recursively axiomatizable theory with no finite models is properly interpretable in some finitely axiomatizable theory with the preservation of all properties from the following list:

1. stability, superstability, and ω-stability;

2. the existence of a strongly constructivizable and autostable prime model;

3. the existence of a strongly constructivizable and autostable minimal model;

4. the existence of a strongly constructivizable homogeneous model;

5. the existence and the strong constructivizability of the countable saturated model;

6. model completeness.

BIBLIOGRAPHY

1. S. S. Goncharov, *Some properties of the constructivization of Boolean algebras*, Sibirsk. Mat. Zh. **16** (1975), 264–278; English transl. in Siberian Math. J. **16** (1975).

2. S. S. Goncharov and A. T. Nurtazin, *Constructive models of complete decidable theories*, Algebra i Logika **12** (1973), 125–142; English transl. in Algebra and Logic **12** (1973).

3. Yu. L. Ershov, *Decision problems and constructivizable models*, "Nauka", Moscow, 1980. (Russian)

4. C. C. Chang and M. J. Keisler, *Model theory*, North-Holland, 1973.

5. A. T. Nurtazin, *Strong and weak constructivizations, and enumerable families*, Algebra i Logika **13** (1974), 311–323; English transl. in Algebra and Logic **13** (1974).

6. M. G. Peretyat'kin, *Example of an ω_1-categorical complete finitely axiomatizable theory*, Algebra i Logika **19** (1980), 314–347; English transl. in Algebra and Logic **19** (1980).

7. ____, *Calculations on Turing machines in finitely axiomatizable theories*, Algebra i Logika **21** (1982), 410–441; English transl. in Algebra and Logic **21** (1982).

8. ____, *Finitely axiomatizable totally transcendental theories*, Trudy Inst. Mat. (Novosibirsk) **2** (1982), 88–135. (Russian)

9. Hartley Rogers, Jr., *Theory of recursive functions and effective computability*, McGraw-Hill, 1967.

10. Lawrence Feiner, *Hierarchies of Boolean algebras*, J. Symbolic Logic **35** (1970), 365–374.

11. William Hanf, *Model-theoretic methods in the study of elementary logic*, Theory of Models (Proc. Internat. Sympos., Berkeley, Calif., 1963; J. W. Addison et al., editors), North-Holland, 1965, pp. 132–145.

12. ____, *The Boolean algebra of logic*, Bull. Amer. Math. Soc. **81** (1975), 587–589.

13. Leo Harrington, *Recursively presentable prime models*, J. Symbolic Logic **39** (1974), 305–309.

14. Alistair H. Lachlan, *The transcendental rank of a theory*, Pacific J. Math. **37** (1971), 119–122.

15. R. L. Vaught, *Sentences true in all constructive models*, J. Symbolic Logic **25** (1960), 39–53.

Institute of Mathematics and Mechanics
Academy of Sciences of the Kazakh SSR
Alma-Ata 480100
USSR

Translated by I. VOICULESCU

Amer. Math. Soc. Transl.
(2) Vol. **147**, 1990

On the Commutator Subgroup
of the Absolute Galois Group

G. V. BELYĬ

In this report we consider one approach to the conjecture that the commutator subgroup $G' = \text{Gal}(\overline{\mathbf{Q}}/\mathbf{Q}_{ab})$ of the Galois group $G = \text{Gal}(\overline{\mathbf{Q}}/\mathbf{Q})$ of the field of all algebraic numbers is a free profinite group. This conjecture was formulated by I. R. Shafarevich.

Suppose H is a finite simple group. We say that a group F is H-*free* if for any exact sequence of finite groups $1 \to H^n \hookrightarrow A \twoheadrightarrow B \to 1$ any epimorphism $F \twoheadrightarrow B$ can be lifted to an epimorphism $F \twoheadrightarrow A$. In other words, there must exist a dashed arrow

$$
\begin{array}{ccc}
 & & F \\
 & \swarrow & \downarrow \\
H^n \hookrightarrow & A & \twoheadrightarrow B
\end{array}
$$

If we can prove that the commutator subgroup G' is H-free for all finite simple groups H, the classification of which was recently obtained, this conjecture will be proved. Iwasawa [I1] proved that the group G' is H-free for all abelian finite simple groups H. For nonabelian finite simple groups H the following result has been proved:

THEOREM 1 (Thompson, Matzat). *If to a Galois tower of coverings $X/\mathbf{P}_1/Y$ defined over the field $\mathbf{Q}_{ab}$ there corresponds the exact sequence of Galois groups $H \hookrightarrow \text{Aut} H \twoheadrightarrow \text{Out} H$, then the commutator subgroup G' is H-free.*

The proof is given in [M1].

Suppose F is a free profinite group on two generators x, y. We define the profinite braid group B as follows:

$$
B = \{\sigma \in \text{Aut} F \,|\, x^\sigma \sim x^\alpha, \, y^\sigma \sim y^\alpha, \, (x, y)^\sigma \sim (xy)^\alpha, \, \alpha \in \widehat{\mathbf{Z}}^* \},
$$

1980 *Mathematics Subject Classification* (1985 *Revision*). Primary 11R32; Secondary 20E05, 20E07, 20E18.

Translation of Proc. Internat. Congr. Math. (Berkeley, Calif., 1986), Vol. 1, Amer. Math. Soc., Providence, R.I., 1987, pp. 346–349; MR **89f**: 12006.

where $\sim$ signifies conjugacy of elements in the group and $\widehat{\mathbf{Z}}^*$ is the multiplicative group of invertible elements of the profinite completion of the ring of integers; we also define subgroups A and A_1:

$$A = \{\sigma \in B | x^\sigma = x^\alpha, y^\sigma = y^{\alpha u}, u \in F'\}, \qquad A_1 = \{\sigma \in A | \alpha = 1\}.$$

It is easy to prove that the centralizers of the generators x and y in the group F are cyclic subgroups isomorphic to $\widehat{\mathbf{Z}}$, and hence $A \cap \operatorname{Int} F = 1$. This means that B is isomorphic to the semidirect product $F \rtimes A$. Moreover, $A/A_1 \cong \widehat{\mathbf{Z}}^*$.

Let $U = \mathbf{P}_1 \backslash \{0, 1, \infty\}$ be the projective line with three points removed, and let K be a maximal extension of the field $\overline{\mathbf{Q}}(t)$ unramified outside these points. Then the Galois group $\operatorname{Gal}(K/\overline{\mathbf{Q}}(t))$, which is the same as the profinite completion of the fundamental group $\pi_1 U(\mathbf{C})$, is isomorphic to the free group F. It turns out that the Galois group $\operatorname{Gal}(K/\mathbf{Q}(t))$ is isomorphic to a semidirect product $F \rtimes \pi(G)$ defined by some homomorphism $\pi\colon G \to A$, and to the tower of fields $\mathbf{Q}(t) \subset \overline{\mathbf{Q}}(t) \subset K$ there corresponds the exact sequence of Galois groups $F \hookrightarrow F \rtimes \pi(G) \twoheadrightarrow G$. This follows easily from the fact that the generators x, y, and xy generate cyclic decomposition subgroups over the rational points 0, 1, ∞, and under the action of elements $\sigma \in \operatorname{Gal}(\overline{\mathbf{Q}}(t)/\mathbf{Q}(t))$ these subgroups are invariant to within conjugation. Furthermore, by considering a maximal abelian subextension of K it is easy to see that $\pi(G') = \pi(G) \cap A_1$.

For an epimorphism $\varphi\colon F \twoheadrightarrow H$ into a finite group we have

THEOREM 2. *If the kernel of the epimorphism φ is invariant under the action of the group A_1 and this action induces only inner automorphisms on the factor-group H, then the Galois covering $X/\mathbf{P}_1$ corresponding to the kernel of this epimorphism can be defined over the field $\mathbf{Q}_{ab}$.*

The proof is an easy consequence of Galois theory; see [B1].

Suppose H is a finite centerless group with two generators a, b. Consider the set M consisting of pairs of generators:

$$M = M(H, a, b) = \{a', b' \in H \mid \langle a', b' \rangle = H, a' \sim a, b' \sim b, a'b' \sim ab\},$$

on which the group H acts by conjugations. If $\#M = \#H$, i.e., the set M consists of one orbit, then the epimorphism $\varphi\colon F \twoheadrightarrow H$ defined by the equalities $\varphi(x) = a$ and $\varphi(y) = b$ satisfies the conditions of Theorem 2. There is a simple way to verify that $\#M = \#H$: it is sufficient that one of the generators of the matrix group H differ from a scalar matrix by a matrix of rank 1. This criterion has enabled the author to establish the existence of extensions $L/\mathbf{Q}_{ab}(t)$ with classical Galois groups; see [B1] and [B2]. Moreover, using the representation theory of finite groups, it is possible to calculate the number $\#M(H, a, b)$ with the aid of the table of characters of the group H and its subgroups. This enabled Thompson, Matzat, and others to establish the existence of such extensions over the field $\mathbf{Q}_{ab}(t)$, and in certain cases even over the field $\mathbf{Q}(t)$, for all sporadic groups except J_4 and also for the groups G_2, $^2G_2$, and $^3D_4$ of Lie type; see the bibliography in [M2]. We should mention that the earliest paper in which these ideas were utilized was [S1], where, in particular, extensions $L/\mathbf{Q}(t)$ with alternating Galois groups were constructed.

It turns out that some of these extensions also satisfy the conditions of Theorem 1. Therefore the group G' is H-free if H is one of the following groups:

(a) an alternating group A_n $(n \neq 6)$;

(b) a group of Lie type A_1, B_n, C_n, D_n, ^2D_n, or G_2 over a prime field; or

(c) a sporadic group, except J_4.

But for many simple groups H the group $\mathrm{Out}\,H$ is not contained in the automorphism group of the projective line $\mathbf{P}_1$. Therefore the next step should probably be a generalization of these theorems to the higher-dimensional case. Theorem 1 is easily generalized if we require that the group $\mathrm{Out}\,H$ act on the projective space $\mathbf{P}_n$ by projective automorphisms. The generalization of Theorem 2 is still an open problem.

The representation $\pi\colon G \to A$ is of interest in its own right. In [B1] we proved

THEOREM 3. *An algebraic curve y can be defined over the field $\overline{\mathbf{Q}}$ if and only if there exists a nonconstant function $\varphi \in \overline{\mathbf{Q}}(y)$ such that the covering $\varphi\colon y \to \mathbf{P}_1$ is ramified over three points.*

This easily implies that the representation π is an embedding. A very interesting problem is to describe its image. Suppose $\psi\colon y \hookrightarrow U^n$ is an embedding defined over $\mathbf{Q}$. Then the image of the étale fundamental group $\pi_1(y)$ in the group $F^n = \pi_1(U^n)$ is invariant to within conjugacy under the action of G. Do all invariants of the action of G on the free group F have, in this sense, a geometric origin?

Suppose F_l is the maximal pro-l-factor-group of F, and $F_{l,m}$ its maximal metabelian factor-group. The representation π induces corresponding representations in the automorphism groups of these groups. Deligne and Ihara obtained very interesting results on these representations; see [I2].

BIBLIOGRAPHY

[B1] G. V. Belyĭ, *On Galois extensions of a maximal cyclotomic field*, Izv. Akad. Nauk SSSR Ser. Mat. **43** (1979), 267–276; English transl. in Math. USSR Izv. **14** (1980), 247–256.

[B2] _____, *On extensions of the maximal cyclotomic field having a given classical Galois group*, J. Reine Angew. Math. **341** (1983), 147–156.

[I1] Kenkichi Iwasawa, *On solvable extensions of algebraic number fields*, Ann. of Math. (2) **58** (1953), 548–572.

[I2] Yasutaka Ihara, *Profinite braid groups, Galois representations and complex multiplications*, Ann. of Math. (2) **123** (1986), 43–106.

[M1]   B. Heinrich Matzat, *Zum Einbettungsproblem der algebraischen Zahlentheorie mit nicht abelschem Kern*, Invent. Math. **80** (1985), 365–374.
[M2]   ____, *Über das Umkehrproblem der Galoisschen Theorie*, Jahresber. Deutsch. Math.-Verein. **90** (1988), 155–183.
[S1]   Kuang-Yen Shih, *On the construction of Galois extensions of function fields and number fields*, Math. Ann. **207** (1974), 99–120.

Vladimir
USSR

Translated by G. A. KANDALL

Amer. Math. Soc. Transl.
(2) Vol. **147**, 1990

Rational Approximations of Analytic Functions

A. A. GONCHAR

This article is an exposition of results on the rate of rational approximation of analytic functions which have been obtained in recent years.

1.

Let E be a compact subset of the extended complex plane $\widehat{\mathbf{C}}$, let f be a continuous function on E, and let $\mathscr{R}_n$ be the class of all rational functions in z of degree not greater than n. Denote by $r_n = r_n(f, E)$ the deviation of f from $\mathscr{R}_n$ (with respect to the uniform metric on E); that is,

$$r_n = \inf\{\|f - r\|_E : r \in \mathscr{R}_n\},$$

where $\|\cdot\|$ is the sup-norm on E. If f is *holomorphic* on the compact set E ($f \in H(E)$), then the sequence r_n tends geometrically to zero; more precisely,

$$\varlimsup_n r_n^{1/n} = q < 1.$$

The number $q = q(f, E)$ is a fundamental measure of the rate of rational approximation of f on E (for $q \in (0, 1)$, in any case). The question of evaluating (characterizing) this number in terms of the analytic continuation of f plays a fundamental role in the theory of rational approximation of analytic functions.

In all that follows we will assume that the compact set E consists of a finite number of nontrivial connected components (continua). Let F be a compact set contained in $\widehat{\mathbf{C}} \backslash E$, and let $h(E, F)$ denote the modulus of the condenser (E, F), i.e., $h = 1/c$, where $c = c(E, F)$ is the capacity of the condenser. The following theorem is a consequence of results of Walsh [15] and Bagby [1] about interpolation by rational functions with *fixed poles*: if

1980 *Mathematics Subject Classification* (1985 *Revision*). Primary 30E10.
Translation of Proc. Internat. Congr. Math. (Berkeley, Calif., 1986), Vol. 1, Amer. Math. Soc., Providence, R.I., 1987, pp. 739–748; MR **89e**: 30066.

the function f is holomorphic in the open set D, and $E \subset D = \widehat{\mathbf{C}} \backslash F$, then the bound

$$q \leq \exp(-h(E, F)) \tag{1}$$

holds for $f(z)$, $z \in E$.

We denote by $\mathscr{F}$ the class of all compact sets F such that the function $f \in H(E)$ has a holomorphic (single-valued analytic) continuation to $\widehat{\mathbf{C}} \backslash F$. We will call the number

$$h = \sup\{h(E, F) : F \in \mathscr{F}\} \qquad (0 < h \leq +\infty)$$

the *modulus of holomorphicity* of the function $f \in H(E)$. In the most interesting cases there exists a unique regular compact set $F_f \in \mathscr{F}$ for which $h(E, F_f) = h$; the open set $D_f = \widehat{\mathbf{C}} \backslash F_f$ is a maximal domain of holomorphicity of the function $f \in H(E)$ (in the plane $\widehat{C}$). It follows from (1) that for any $f \in H(E)$ the numbers q and h are related by the inequality

$$q \leq e^{-h}. \tag{2}$$

We note that both of the characteristic quantities q and h are invariant with respect to linear fractional transformations of the plane $\widehat{\mathbf{C}}$.

The bound (2) allows one to evaluate q only when $h = +\infty$. This condition means that the function $f \in H(E)$ can be continued holomorphically to a domain of the form $\widehat{\mathbf{C}} \backslash F$, where $\operatorname{cap} F = 0$ (cap denotes logarithmic capacity); for such functions

$$q = \lim_n r_n^{1/n} = 0.$$

In the general case one cannot describe the number q in terms of the analytic continuation of f alone; in particular, q cannot be expressed in terms of h. There are well-known examples of functions for which $0 < q = e^{-h}$, but these functions are of a rather exotic nature. Several results obtained in recent years show that for large classes of analytic functions, which include the most important functions of analysis, q can be calculated from h, and in addition

$$q = \lim_n r_n^{1/n} = e^{-2h}. \tag{3}$$

Apparently, the first results of a general nature reducing to formula (3) were obtained by the author in [2] and [3] by means of a method based on the interpolation of a function $f \in H(E)$ by rational functions with *free poles* (the method of multipoint Padé approximants). In [2] we considered the case in which E and F are segments of the real line $\mathbf{R}$ and

$$f(z) = \int_F \frac{d\sigma(t)}{z - t}, \qquad z \in E,$$

where σ is a positive measure whose support is contained in F. The main result of that paper is that

$$q = \exp(-2h(E, F)) \tag{4}$$

provided that $\sigma' = d\sigma/dt > 0$ almost everywhere on F. The modulus $h(E, F)$ can be expressed in terms of complete elliptic integrals of the first kind; if $E = [a, b]$ and $F = [c, d]$, then

$$h(E, F) = \pi K'/K, \qquad k^2 = \frac{(a-b)(c-d)}{(d-b)(c-a)}.$$

In [3] formula (4) was proved in the case when E is compact and symmetric with respect to $\mathbf{R}$, F is the union of a finite number of segments of $\mathbf{R}$, and f is holomorphic in the domain $D = \widehat{\mathbf{C}}\backslash F$ and has a sufficiently regular jump across F. It follows from the main theorem of [3] that equation (3) holds for any function $f \in H(E)$ which permits analytic continuation along paths which lie in a domain of the form $\widehat{\mathbf{C}}\backslash e$, where e is a compact subset of $\mathbf{R}$ of zero capacity.

We pause to sketch the manner in which multipoint Padé approximants are applied to the problem of the rate of uniform approximation of analytic functions; see [3] for additional details. Let $f \in H(E)$, let $\alpha = \{\alpha_{n,k}\}$, $k = 1, 2, \ldots, n$, $n = 1, 2, \ldots$, be a triangular array of points (interpolation nodes) which belong to the compact set E, and let

$$A_n(z) = (z - \alpha_{n,1}) \cdots (z - \alpha_{n,n}).$$

We fix a natural number n and consider the rational function $R_n = P_n/Q_n$, where P_n and Q_n are arbitrary polynomials in z which satisfy

$$\deg P_n \le n - 1, \quad \deg Q_n \le n \quad (Q_n \not\equiv 0); \qquad \frac{Q_n f - P_n}{A_{2n}} \in H(E). \qquad (5)$$

The latter requirement means that $Q_n f - P_n = 0$ at the points of the $2n$th row of the array α (counting multiplicities). Polynomials satisfying (5) exist for any $f \in H(E)$. Their quotient P_n/Q_n defines a unique rational function R_n (to within the usual identification). This rational function is called the *multipoint Padé approximant* (of type $[n - \frac{1}{n}]$ of the function f corresponding to the array α of interpolation nodes. If $Q_n \ne 0$ at the nodes $\alpha_{2n,1}, \ldots, \alpha_{2n,2n}$, then R_n interpolates f at these points. In the contrary case, upon passing from $Q_n f - P_n$ to $f - R_n$ some of the interpolation conditions are lost; however, the loss of d_n interpolation conditions is accompanied by a reduction of d_n in the degrees of the numerator and denominator of R_n. The basic difficulties involved in applying multipoint Padé approximants (corresponding to a given array of interpolation nodes) lie in the analysis of the asymptotic behavior of the poles and of the convergence of the approximants themselves. If the function $f \in H(E)$ can be holomorphically continued to the open set $D = \widehat{\mathbf{C}}\backslash F$ (without loss of generality one can assume that E and F are compact in $\mathbf{C}$ and $f(\infty) = 0$), then the polynomials Q_n satisfy the complex orthogonality relation

$$\int_\gamma Q_n(t) t^j \frac{f(t)\, dt}{A_{2n}(t)} = 0, \qquad j = 0, 1, \ldots, n-1, \qquad (6)$$

where γ is an arbitrary contour which surrounds F (γ lies in the complement of $E \cup F$). For the difference $f - R_n$ we have

$$(f - R_n)(z) = \frac{1}{2\pi i} \cdot \frac{A_{2n}(z)}{(Q_n Q)(z)} \int_\gamma \frac{(Q_n Q f)(t)\, dt}{A_{2n}(t)(z - t)}, \qquad (7)$$

where Q is an arbitrary polynomial of degree not greater than n. When F consists of a set of smooth contours (slits) in $\mathbf{C}$ and the function f has a sufficiently regular jump across F, the orthogonality relations (6) can be written in the form

$$\int_F Q_n(t) t^j \cdot \frac{\chi(t)\, dt}{A_{2n}(t)} = 0, \qquad j = 0, 1, \ldots, n - 1 \qquad (8)$$

(χ denotes the jump in f across F); (7) can be rewritten similarly.

The application of (6) or (8) for the analysis of the limit distribution of the zeros of the polynomials Q_n is complicated by two circumstances. First, in the most interesting cases (for example, when the element $f \in H(E)$ defines a multi-valued analytic function with a finite number of branch points) the domain of holomorphicity $D = \mathbf{C} \backslash F$ of f and, by the same token, the set of slits F determined by f are not uniquely defined; second, the measure $f(t)\, dt / A_{2n}(t)$ in the orthogonality relations for Q_n depends on the index of Q_n (this dependence is related to the choice of the array of interpolation nodes). The results we have (something will be said about them below) show that the zeros of Q_n (the poles of R_n) "pick out" a set of slits which have a certain "symmetry" property with respect to E and α, if the properties of f allow such a choice; the limit distribution of the zeros of Q_n on this set of slits also depends on properties of the array α. We note that many concrete problems in this direction still remain open.

We return to the problem under discussion. Let $\lambda = \lambda_F - \lambda_E$ be the equilibrium charge on the condenser (E, F) (λ_E and λ_F are unit measures concentrated on E and F, respectively), and let $V = V^\lambda$ be the logarithmic potential of the charge λ:

$$V^\lambda(z) = \int \log \frac{1}{|t - z|} d\lambda(t), \qquad z \in \mathbf{C}.$$

In the case when E is compact and symmetric with respect to $\mathbf{R}$, F is a set of segments of $\mathbf{R}$, and the function $f \in H(D)$, where $D = \mathbf{C} \backslash F$, has a regular (e.g., analytic) jump across F, the following statement is true.

(*) *If the points of the array α have a limit distribution characterized by the measure λ_E, then the zeros of Q_n (poles of R_n) also have a limit distribution, and this limit distribution is characterized by the measure λ_F; the sequence R_n converges to f in capacity (on compact subsets) inside the domain D, and moreover,*

$$|f - R_n|^{1/n} \to \exp 2(V - h_F) \qquad (9)$$

in capacity inside D; *here* h_F *is the value of* V *on* F (*so that the right-hand side of* (9) *is equal to* e^{-2h}, *where* $h = h_F - h_E = h(E, F)$, *on* E).

This assertion plays a key role in the application of multipoint Padé approximants to problems on the rate of uniform approximation by rational functions. In [3] it was shown that formula (4) already follows from it (the proof of the inequality $q = \overline{\lim} \, r_n^{1/n} \le e^{-2h}$ is not difficult; in [3] it is proved that the inequality $q = \underline{\lim} \, r_n^{1/n} \ge e^{-2h}$ also follows from (9)). In the case in which the jump of f across F is given by a positive measure σ, the analysis becomes considerably simpler; in this case the polynomials Q_n satisfy the corresponding orthogonality relations of the form

$$\int_F Q_n(t) t^j \frac{d\sigma(t)}{A_{2n}(t)} = 0, \qquad j = 0, 1, \ldots, n-1$$

(with weights which depend on the index of the polynomial). A general theorem on the limit distribution of the zeros of such polynomials was obtained in [6]; for the case considered above the corresponding result is contained in [5].

A major development for problems involving the limit distribution of the poles and the convergence of the Padé approximants was obtained by H. Stahl [10]–[12]. Stahl's main result deals with the case in which E is a continuum with connected complement and f can be continued along any path that lies in a domain of the form $\hat{C}\backslash e$, where e is a compact set of zero capacity (this is of interest when the element $f \in H(E)$ defines a multi-valued function in this domain). In this case there exists a unique domain D, $E \subset D = \hat{C}\backslash F$, such that $h(E, F) = h$ and D contains any other domain of holomorphicity of f which also maximizes the modulus (h is the modulus of holomorphicity of f, $F = F_f$, and $D = D_f$). Stahl proved that assertion (*) holds for the multipoint Padé approximants of the functions $f \in H(E)$ under consideration (with $F = F_f$ and $D = D_f$). As noted above, (4) with $F = F_f$ already follows from this, and consequently (3) also holds for an arbitrary $f \in H(E)$ which defines a multi-valued analytic function the set of whose singular points has capacity zero. Stahl's method is based on the fact that the compact set $F = F_f$ (the set of slits) and consequently the maximal domain of holomorphicity $D = D_f$ have a specific "symmetry" property with respect to E. In this regard the property of unrestricted continuability of f in $\hat{C}\backslash e$ is not essential; the only thing that is important is that f have a sufficiently regular jump on F_f. It is convenient to formulate the corresponding general theorem as a theorem on the rate of approximation of holomorphic functions on "symmetric" (with respect to E) open sets $D = \hat{C}\backslash F$ (see the following section, where in contrast to this section we give precise definitions and statements of the theorems).

2.

A point ζ of the compact set F will be called *regular* if it has a neighborhood $U(\zeta)$ whose intersection with F is a simple analytic arc. The set of all regular points of a compact set F is denoted by F_0. We will denote by $\mathscr{A}$ the class of all compact sets F such that $\text{cap}(F\backslash F_0) = 0$ and $F_0 \neq \varnothing$.

We consider a condenser (E, F) and write $F \in S(E)$ (and say that the compact set F and the open set $D = \widehat{\mathbf{C}}\backslash F$ have *property* S with respect to E) if $F \in \mathscr{A}$ and

$$\frac{\partial V}{\partial n}(\zeta^1) = \frac{\partial V}{\partial n}(\zeta^2), \qquad \forall \zeta \in F_0; \tag{10}$$

here V is the equilibrium potential for the condenser (E, F), ζ^1 and ζ^2 are the accessible boundary points of D which correspond to the point $\zeta \in F_0$, and $\partial/\partial n$ denotes differentiation in the direction of the normal to F which points into D.

One can describe a general construction of compact sets $F \in S(E)$ in the following manner. We fix E (recall that the compact sets being considered are unions of a finite number of continua $E_1, \ldots, E_N$) and a compact set $e \subset \widehat{\mathbf{C}}$ of capacity zero which does not intersect E. We consider any Riemann surface $\mathscr{R}$ which is a two-sheeted (unramified) covering surface of $\widehat{\mathbf{C}}\backslash e$, and denote the corresponding projection by p. Let E^1 and E^2 be nonintersecting compact subsets of $\mathscr{R}$ such that $p(E^j) = E$, $j = 1, 2$, and let $\omega(\tilde{z})$, $\tilde{z} \in \Omega = \mathscr{R}\backslash(E^1 \cup E^2)$, be the harmonic measure of ∂E^1 with respect to Ω. Then the closure F of the set $p\{\tilde{z} \in \mathscr{R}: \omega(\tilde{z}) = 1/2\}$ belongs to $S(E)$.

It is well known that many extremal problems in geometric function theory lead to compact sets F and open sets D which have property S.

Let $F \in \mathscr{A}$, and let f be a holomorphic function on the open set $D = \widehat{\mathbf{C}}\backslash F$. We write $f \in H_0(D)$ if for any point $\zeta \in F_0\backslash e_0$ (where e_0 is a compact set of capacity zero) the limits

$$\lim_{z \to \zeta^j, z \in D} f(z) = f(\zeta^j), \qquad j = 1, 2,$$

exist, and in addition, $f(\zeta^1) \neq f(\zeta^2)$ (as above, ζ^1 and ζ^2 are the accessible boundary points of D which correspond to the point ζ, so that the difference $f(\zeta^1) - f(\zeta^2)$ gives the jump of f at the point ζ).

THEOREM 1. *Let (E, F) be a condenser such that $F \in S(E)$, and let f belong to $H_0(D)$, where $D = \widehat{\mathbf{C}}\backslash F$. Then*

$$q = \lim_n r_n^{1/n} = e^{-2h(E, F)}.$$

We single out two corollaries of this theorem (the first of which has already been mentioned in §1 in connection with Stahl's results).

Equation (3) holds in each of the following cases:

(i) E is a continuum and the element $f \in H(E)$ defines a multi-valued analytic function with a finite number of singular points;

(ii) E is a union of pairwise disjoint continua $E_1, \ldots, E_N$, and $f(z) = c_j$ for $z \in E_j$, $j = 1, \ldots, N$ (the case $N = 2$ corresponds to a classical problem of Zolotarëv; see [4]).

Theorem 1 reduces the solution of many other problems about the rate of rational approximation of analytic functions to problems in geometric function theory associated with the characterization of the maximal domain of holomorphicity (different versions of the modulus problem).

Before formulating the next theorem we introduce some necessary concepts and notation. Let (E, F) be a condenser with $F \in \mathscr{A}$, and assume for simplicity that E and F are compact subsets of $\mathbf{C}$ and that F is the union of a finite number of analytic Jordan arcs (such that $F \backslash F_0$ is a finite set). We consider a fixed function φ which is harmonic in some neighborhood of F. We denote by $M(E, F)$ the set of all charges of the form $\mu = \mu_F - \mu_E$, where μ_E and μ_F are unit measures concentrated on E and F, respectively. One can show that there exists a unique charge $\lambda \in M(E, F)$ such that

$$V^\lambda(z) \equiv w_1, \qquad z \in E,$$

$$(V^\lambda + \varphi)(z) \equiv \min_F(V^\lambda + \varphi) = w_2, \qquad z \in L = \operatorname{supp} \lambda_F; \tag{11}$$

the constants w_1 and w_2 are also uniquely defined by the equilibrium relation (11). We set $w = w(E, F, \varphi) = w_2 - w_1$.

The charge $\lambda = \lambda_F - \lambda_E$ solves the equilibrium problem on (E, F) provided that the plate F lies in the external field φ. We note that the equilibrium charge λ is the unique solution to the following energy minimalization problem:

$$I_\varphi(\lambda) = \inf\{I_\varphi(\mu) : \mu \in M(E, F)\},$$

where

$$I_\varphi(\mu) = \int \log \frac{1}{|t - z|} d\mu(t) \, d\mu(z) + 2 \int \varphi(t) \, d\mu_F(t).$$

See [7] for more general equilibrium problems in the presence of external fields. In these problems one is given compact sets (conductors) $F_1, \ldots, F_m$, the magnitude of the charge on each of these conductors, an $m \times m$ matrix $A = \|a_{jk}\|$ which describes the interaction between the charges placed on the different conductors, and external fields $\varphi_1, \ldots, \varphi_m$ in these conductors. The solution of several problems associated with rational approximation of analytic functions can be formulated in terms of the corresponding equilibrium distributions.

We return to the problem formulated in (11). We write $F \in S(E, \varphi)$ if $L = \operatorname{supp} \lambda_F \in \mathscr{A}$ and

$$\frac{\partial(V^\lambda + \varphi)}{\partial n}(\zeta^1) = \frac{\partial(V^\lambda + \varphi)}{\partial n}(\zeta^2)$$

at each point $\zeta \in L_0$ (the notation has the same meaning as in (10)).

THEOREM 2. *Let* $F \in S(E, \varphi)$, *and let* g_n *be a sequence of functions which are holomorphic in a neighborhood* U *of the compact set* F *and such that* $(1/2n)\operatorname{Re} g_n \rightrightarrows \varphi$ *inside* U. *The relation*

$$\lim_n r_n(f_n, E)^{1/n} = e^{-2w} \tag{12}$$

holds for the sequence of functions

$$f_n(z) = \int_F \frac{e^{-g_n(t)} dt}{z - t}, \qquad z \in E,$$

where $w = w(E, F, \varphi)$.

Relation (12) holds in the somewhat more general setting in which

$$f_n(z) = \int_\gamma \frac{e^{-g_n(t)} dt}{z - t}, \qquad z \in E,$$

where $f \in H_0(D)$ and γ is an arbitrary contour which lies in U and which surrounds the compact set F (the functions $f_n(z)$, $z \in E$, do not depend on γ).

Theorem 2 has an immediate application to the problem of the rate of rational approximation of the exponential function on the semiaxis. We set $\rho_n = r_n(e^{-x}, E^+)$, where $E^+ = [0, \infty]$. A detailed survey of results of the form

$$0 < c_1 \le \varliminf_n \rho_n^{1/n} \le \varlimsup_r \rho_r^{1/n} \le c_2 < 1$$

and of conjectures concerning the existence and value of $v = \lim \rho_n^{1/2}$ is to be found in the book of Varga [14]. Using the Carathéodory-Fejér method which was adapted to rational approximation of real functions on $[-1, 1]$ by Trefethen and Gutknecht [13], A. Magnus [8] recently determined that the value of the constant v is $\exp(-\pi K'/K)$, where K is the complete elliptic integral of the first kind whose modulus is defined by $K(k) = 2E(k)$. The method of determining the value of v described in [8] is in its main points heuristic in nature; it is not yet clear how to rigorously justify the transition from n-fold integrals to the limit distribution (for $n \to \infty$). Nuttall used this kind of transition for the analysis of the asymptotic properties of Hermite-Padé polynomials (Nuttall's saddle-point method; see [9]); the justification of the method reduces to the solution of a series of problems in the theory of rational approximation which at this point remain unsolved.

Using Theorem 2, one can prove that $v = \lim \rho_n^{1/n}$ exists and describe the number v in terms of equilibrium problems for a condenser of the form (E^+, F) under the condition that the plate F (an analytic arc symmetric with respect to $\mathbf{R}$) lies in the external field $\varphi(z) = \frac{1}{2}\operatorname{Re} z$, where $F \in S(E^+, \frac{1}{2}\operatorname{Re} z)$. The solution of this equilibrium problem can be given in terms of elliptic functions and integrals. In this way one can obtain the

following very simple characterization of the number v : v *is the (unique)*
positive root of the equation

$$\sum_{n=1}^{\infty} a_n x^n = \frac{1}{8}, \quad a_n = \left| \sum_{d \mid n} (-1)^d d \right|. \tag{13}$$

If $n = 2^m p_1^{m_1} \cdots p_s^{m_s}$ is the canonical representation of the number n (the p_j are odd primes, $m \geq 0$, and $m_j \geq 1$), then

$$a_n = |2^{m+1} - 3| \frac{p_1^{m_1+1} - 1}{p_1 - 1} \cdots \frac{p_s^{m_s+1} - 1}{p_s - 1}.$$

Calculation of the constant v based on (13) is not difficult; we have

$$1/v = 9.28902549192081891875544943595174506103 17 \ldots$$

(this number is given to 13 places in [8]). In the same manner it is possible to study very general problems about the exponential function, in particular that of characterizing the number

$$v_\theta = \lim_n r_n(e^{-z}, E_\theta), \qquad E_\theta = \{z = re^{it} : r \geq 0, |t| \leq \theta < \pi/2\}.$$

Theorems 1 and 2 and the results on the exponential function were obtained by the author jointly with E. A. Rakhmanov. The theorems are proved by the multipoint Padé approximant method of [3]; the arrays of interpolation nodes are constructed from measures λ_E which appear in the corresponding equilibrium problems. The necessary asymptotic properties of the multipoint Padé approximants are established by an appropriate modification of Stahl's method. Another version of Theorem 1 has also been obtained by Stahl.

BIBLIOGRAPHY

1. Thomas Bagby, *On interpolation by rational functions*, Duke Math. J. **36** (1969), 95–104.

2. A. A. Gonchar, *On the rate of rational approximation of some analytic functions*, Mat. Sb. **105 (147)** (1978), 147–163; English transl. in Math. USSR Sb. **34** (1978).

3. ____, *On the rate of rational approximation of analytic functions*, Trudy Mat. Inst. Steklov. **166** (1984), 52–60; English transl. in Proc. Steklov Inst. Math. **1986**, no. 1 (166).

4. ____, *Zolotarëv problems connected with rational functions*, Mat. Sb. **78 (120)** (1969), 640–654; English transl. in Math. USSR Sb. **7** (1969).

5. A. A. Gonchar and Giermo Lopes L. [Guillermo López L.], *On Markov's theorem for multipoint Padé aprproximants*, Mat. Sb. **105 (147)** (1978), 512–524; English transl. in Math. USSR Sb. **34** (1978).

6. A. A. Gonchar and E. A. Rakhmanov, *Equilibrium measure and the distribution of zeros of extremal polynomials*, Mat. Sb. **125 (167)** (1984), 117–127; English transl. in Math. USSR Sb. **53** (1986).

7. ____, *On the equilibrium problem for vector potentials*, Uspekhi Mat. Nauk **40** (1985), no. 4 (244), 155–156; English transl. in Russian Math. Surveys **40** (1985).

8. A. P. Magnus, *CFGT determination of Varga's constant "1/9"*, Preprint, Inst. Math., Univ. Catholique de Louvain, Louvain-La-Neuve, 1986.

9. J. Nuttall, *Asymptotics of diagonal Hermite-Padé polynomials*, J. Approximation Theory **42** (1984), 299–386.

10. Herbert Stahl, *The convergence of Padé approximants to functions with branch points*, J. Approximation Theory (to appear).

11. ____, *On the convergence of generalized Padé approximants*, Constructive Approximation **5** (1989), 221–240.

12. ____, *A note on three conjectures by Gonchar on rational approximation*, J. Approximation Theory **50** (1987), 3–7.

13. Lloyd N. Trefethen and Martin H. Gutknecht, *The Carathéodory-Fejer method for real rational approximation*, SIAM J. Numer. Anal. **20** (1983), 420–436.

14. Richard S. Varga, *Topics in polynomial and rational interpolation and approximation*, Sém Math. Sup., vol. 81, Presses Univ. Montréal, Montréal, 1982.

15. J. L. Walsh, *Interpolation and approximation by rational functions in the complex domain*, 2nd ed., Amer. Math. Soc., Providence, R.I., 1956.

Steklov Mathematical Institute
Moscow 117966
USSR

Translated by J. GEVIRTZ

Amer. Math. Soc. Transl.
(2) Vol. **147**, 1990

Probability in the Geometry of Banach Spaces

E. D. GLUSKIN

This article is devoted to some results in the geometry of Banach spaces obtained by using probability-theoretic considerations. The classical way of proving the existence of objects having special properties by determining that they fill a set of large measure was intensively employed in the geometry of Banach spaces in the mid-1970's. By that time sufficiently intuitive probabilistic proofs of Dvoretzky's theorem on almost Euclidean sections of convex bodies had been found (Milman [38], Figiel [14], Szandowski [52]), and Enflo's famous example [13] of a space without the approximation property, the construction of which acquired a probabilistic character almost at once, had appeared (Davie [11]; see also Mityagin [39]). Considerable interest in the study of finite-dimensional normed spaces (in other words, Minkowski spaces) emerged at roughly the same time. Many questions in the theory of Banach spaces received interesting interpretations on the finite-dimensional level, and many infinite-dimensional problems were solved by "gluing together" finite-dimensional results. Presenting itself first and foremost was the problem of the existence of finite-dimensional spaces and operators with specific properties. By studying the norms of random matrices with elements taking the values ± 1 independently with probability $1/2$, Bennett, Goodman, and Newman [3] completed a description of the classes of (p, q)-absolutely summing operators on a Hilbert space. A further study of a random subspace—the range of such a matrix—enabled them, jointly with Dor and Johnson [2], to construct an example of an uncomplemented Hilbert subspace of the space L_p for $1 < p < 2$. Using randomly chosen subspaces for uniform approximation of the Euclidean ball, Kashin [32] was able to get estimates of the widths $d_n(B_p^N, l_q^N)$ (see the definition below) that are sharp

1980 *Mathematics Subject Classification* (1985 *Revision*). Primary 46-02, 46B20, 60B99; Secondary 46B15.

Translation of Proc. Internat. Congr. Math. (Berkeley, Calif., 1986), Vol. 2, Amer. Math. Soc., Providence, R.I., 1987, pp. 924–938; MR **89h**: 46025.

on the power scale (as well as sharp orders when $n \asymp N$). That settled the old question of the orders of the widths of Sobolev classes. An investigation of the imbeddings in Kashin's paper enabled Figiel, Kwapień, and Pełczyński [16] to construct for each n an n-dimensional space for which every basis has unconditionality constant of order at least $\sqrt{n}$, i.e., an n-dimensional space with the worst unconditional basis constant with respect to order. (See also the development of this result by Figiel and Johnson [15].) We could go on and on with the list of results in Banach geometry in which probabilistic considerations play a decisive role. Since that is not possible here, we dwell in detail on the following two questions: (1) the stochastic selection of Minkowski spaces with special properties; and (2) the use of random subspaces for estimating widths. Unfortunately, the framework of this survey does not encompass investigations on factorization of random operators (see, for example, [4] and [10]), investigations bordering on Dvoretzky's theorem (see [17], and Milman's papers of recent years and their bibliographies), in particular, the elegant proof of Mazur's conjecture given by Bourgain and Mil′man [8], the remarkable results (going back to Kadets [29]) of Johnson and Schechtman [28] and Pisier [45] on imbeddings of spaces, and so on.

0. Standard notation

Below, $\langle \cdot, \cdot \rangle$ is an inner product, vol or vol_n is the Lebesgue volume in $\mathbf{R}^n$, $S^{n-1} \subset \mathbf{R}^n$ is the unit sphere, and μ_n is Lebesgue measure on S^{n-1}, normalized by the condition $\mu_n(S^{n-1}) = 1$.

The standard Gaussian measure on $\mathbf{R}^n$ is determined by the density

$$(2\pi)^{-n/2} \exp\left(-\sum_1^n x_i^2/2\right)$$

and denoted by γ_n. The manifold of all n-dimensional subspaces of $\mathbf{R}^n$ is denoted by $G_{n,N}$, and $\mu_{n,N}$ is the unitarily invariant probability measure on $G_{n,N}$.

Let l_p^n be the n-dimensional (real or complex, depending on the context) normed space with the norm

$$\|x\|_p = \left(\sum_{i=1}^n |x_i|^p\right)^{1/p}, \quad 1 \le p < \infty; \qquad \|x\|_\infty = \max_{1 \le i \le n} |x_i|.$$

The unit ball of this space is denoted by B_p^n. The letter c stands for positive constants, different at different places. The notation $O(\cdot)$ and $o(\cdot)$ is used in the standard way. Sometimes we write $\varphi \prec \psi$ instead of $\varphi = O(\psi)$.

The expression $\varphi \asymp \psi$ means that $\varphi \prec \psi$ and $\psi \prec \varphi$.

1. Finite-dimensional spaces with special properties

Let X and Y be isomorphic Banach spaces. The quantity

$$d(X, Y) = \inf\{\|T\|\,\|T^{-1}\| : T : X \to Y \text{ a linear isomorphism}\}$$

is called the *Banach-Mazur distance* between spaces X and Y. The collection of all normed spaces of fixed dimension n is a compact metric space with the measure of closeness $\log d(\cdot, \cdot)$. It is called the *Minkowski compactum* and denoted by $\mathfrak{M}_n$.

QUESTION. How does the quantity

$$\operatorname{diam} \mathfrak{M}_n = \sup\{d(X, Y) : X, Y \in \mathfrak{M}_n\} \tag{1}$$

behave as n increases? The exact value of $\operatorname{diam} \mathfrak{M}_n$ is known only for the case $n = 2$: $\operatorname{diam} \mathfrak{M}_2 = 3/2$ (Stromquist [49]). A classical result of John [27] shows that $\sup\{d(X, l_2^n) : X \in \mathfrak{M}_n\} = \sqrt{n}$. This implies immediately that for all $X, Y \in \mathfrak{M}_n$

$$d(X, Y) \leq d(X, l_2^n)d(l_2^n, Y) \leq n.$$

Thus, $\sqrt{n} \leq \operatorname{diam} \mathfrak{M}_n \leq n$. Restriction of the supremum in (1) to various subsets of $\mathfrak{M}_n$ leads to many interesting problems. It is usually possible to get an estimate of order $\sqrt{n}$ (see, for example, [58], [59], [12], [9]). This is the case, for instance, when the spaces X and Y have a 1-symmetric basis (Tomczak-Jaegermann [59]). The use of probabilistic considerations has proved to be very fruitful for obtaining such estimates (see, for example, [58] and [12]): a probability measure is introduced on the set of operators T implementing an isomorphism between X and Y. When it is appropriately chosen, the problem of estimating the expectation of the value $\|T\|\,\|T^{-1}\|$ with respect to this measure turns out to be relatively simple and leads to the desired result about the size of $d(X, Y)$.

Let us make a naive attempt to apply this approach to the case $X = Y = l_1^n$, specifying Gaussian measure on the set of linear isomorphisms (this means that an operator T is given by a matrix (t_{ij}) whose elements are independent standard Gaussian variables). It is not hard to see that the inequality $\|T\|\,\|T^{-1}\| \succ n$ holds in this case with large probability. This suggests that by "spoiling" the space l_1^n a little it is possible to construct spaces X and Y such that $\|T\|\,\|T^{-1}\| > cn$ ($c > 0$ an absolute constant) for every isomorphism $T : X \to Y$. This is actually the case.

THEOREM 1 [19]. $\operatorname{diam} \mathfrak{M}_n \asymp n$.

As already noted, the estimate $\operatorname{diam} \mathfrak{M}_n \prec n$ follows from John's theorem.

However, so far no one has been able to give an explicit description of spaces $X_n, Y_n \in \mathfrak{M}_n$ such that $d(X_n, Y_n) > cn$ with some absolute constant $c > 0$. A stochastic selection of spaces X_n and Y_n is used to prove Theorem

1. To realize such an approach on $\mathfrak{M}_n \times \mathfrak{M}_n$ it is necessary to introduce a probability measure and prove that the inequality $d(X, Y) > cn$ holds with positive probability. At present the structure of the compactum $\mathfrak{M}_n$ has been little studied; in particular, it is not clear what the most natural measures on $\mathfrak{M}_n$ (and on $\mathfrak{M}_n \times \mathfrak{M}_n$) are. For our purposes the following probability $\mathscr{P}$ on $\mathfrak{M}_n \times \mathfrak{M}_n$ proves to be convenient (its definition was inspired by the arguments before the formulation of Theorem 1).

With a sequence $F = (f_1, \ldots, f_{2n})$ of elements of $\mathbf{R}^n$ we associate the space $X_F \in \mathfrak{M}_n$ whose unit ball coincides with the set

$$A_F = \mathrm{conv}\{B_1^n, \pm f_1, \ldots, \pm f_{2n}\}.$$

The measure ν on $\mathfrak{M}_n$ is induced under the mapping $F \to X_F$ when the elements $f_1, \ldots, f_{2n}$ are randomly and independently chosen from (S^{n-1}, μ_n). The measure $\mathscr{P}$ is equal to $\nu \times \nu$.

PROPOSITION 1. *There exists an absolute constant $c > 0$ such that if the space Y belongs to the support of the measure ν, then the ν-measure of those $X \in \mathfrak{M}_n$ such that there is an operator T from X to Y with norm $\|T\| \leq c\sqrt{n}|\det T|^{1/n}$ is less than 2^{-n^2}.*

Both the X and the Y of Proposition 1 are spaces of type X_F. Such a space is a specially normed $\mathbf{R}^n$. Thus, both X and Y have a fixed basis, and this permits us to identify each operator from X to Y with the corresponding matrix. We can therefore speak of the determinant of an operator and of its action in another pair of spaces of the same form.

Theorem 1 can be derived immediately from Proposition 1. Its proof is divided into two relatively independent parts. First, it is proved that

$$\nu\{X \in \mathfrak{M}_n : \|S\|_{X \to Y} \leq 2\varepsilon\sqrt{n}\} \leq (A\varepsilon^2)^{n^2} \tag{2}$$

for every operator S with $|\det S| = 1$ and every $\varepsilon > 0$ (A is an absolute constant). Second, a finite set $\mathscr{M}$ of operators with $\mathrm{Card}\,\mathscr{M} \leq (A/\varepsilon)^{n^2}$ is chosen that depends only on Y and ε and is such that if there exist a space X in the support of ν and an operator T from X to Y with norm $\|T\|_{X \to Y} \leq \varepsilon\sqrt{n}|\det T|^{1/n}$, then there is an operator $S \in \mathscr{M}$ such that $|\det S| = 1$ and $\|S - |\det T|^{-1/n}T\|_{X \to Y} \leq \varepsilon\sqrt{n}$ (it is automatic that $\|S\|_{X \to Y} \leq 2\varepsilon\sqrt{n}$).

Comparison of (2) with the cardinality of $\mathscr{M}$ for $\varepsilon = c = \frac{1}{2}A^2$ proves Proposition 1.

The proof of (2) is easily derived from the independence of the vectors $f_1, \ldots, f_{2n}$ determining the unit ball of the random space $X = X_F$, and from the following estimate of the distribution on (S^{n-1}, μ_n) of the random variable $\|Sf\|_Y$ in terms of the Lebesgue volume $\mathrm{vol}\,BY$ of the unit ball of Y:

$$\mu_n\{f \in S^{n-1} : \|Sf\|_Y \leq \lambda\} \leq \lambda^n |\det S|^{-1} \mathrm{vol}\,BY / \mathrm{vol}\,B_2^n. \tag{3}$$

This inequality is used with $\lambda = 2\varepsilon\sqrt{n}$, and $\mathrm{vol}\,BY$ can be estimated by using the fact the unit ball of Y has a small number of boundary points (see [33]).

The inequality (3) was first discovered and used in Banach geometry by Szarek [56]. It lay at the basis of the important concept (introduced by Szarek and Tomczak-Jaegermann [57]) of the "volume ratio of Minkowski spaces".

The set $\mathscr{M}$ is taken to be a minimal ε-net (in the metric generated by the l_2^n-operator norm) of the set of matrices T such that $\|T\|_{l_1^n \to Y} \le 1$ and $|\det T| = 1$.

REMARKS. 1. The support of the measure ν is a very special subset of $\mathfrak{M}_n$—it is a quotient space of l_1^{3n}. In other words, ν can be regarded as a probability on the manifold $G_{2n,3n}$ of all $2n$-dimensional subspaces of l_1^{3n}. With this viewpoint it is more customary to consider the measure $\tilde{\nu}$ on $G_{2n,3n}$ which is unitarily invariant in the l_2^{3n}-sense. It differs from ν, but is fairly close to it and also can be used to prove Theorem 1. To define $\tilde{\nu}$ in terms analogous to ν we must consider the sets $\mathrm{conv}\{\pm f_1, \dots, \pm f_{3n}\}$ instead of the sets A_F, and choose the elements $f_1, \dots, f_{3n}$ independently in $(\mathbf{R}^n, \gamma_n)$. The closeness of ν and $\tilde{\nu}$ is due to the facts that, first, the Gaussian vector f_n is distributed mainly in a neighborhood of the sphere $\sqrt{n}S^{n-1}$ for large n, and, second, the volume of the "octahedral" set $\mathrm{conv}\{\pm f_1, \dots, \pm f_n\}$ turns out to be fairly large with probability close to 1 when $f_1, \dots, f_n$ run through $(\mathbf{R}^n, \gamma_n)$ independently.

2. By analogy with the definitions of ν and $\tilde{\nu}$ it is natural to introduce the measures $\nu_{k,B}$ and $\tilde{\nu}_{k,B}$ on $\mathfrak{M}_n$. Their definitions differ in that k points are taken instead of $2n$ points $f_1, \dots, f_{2n}$, and the "octahedron" B_1^n is replaced by another convex centrally symmetric body B. There are various interesting questions concerning the random Minkowski spaces that arise in this way. One of the simplest is the question of estimating the mean values of functionals on $\mathfrak{M}_n$ that are interesting for this or that reason.

In [24] Gordon introduced the following concept describing the degree of symmetry of Minkowski spaces. The asymmetry constant $s(X)$ ($X \in \mathfrak{M}_n$) is defined to be the infimum of the numbers λ with the following property: there exists a group G of invertible linear operators on X such that each operator commuting with all $g \in G$ has the form $a \cdot \mathrm{Id}$ (Id is the identity operator), and $\sup\{\|g\| : g \in G\} \le \lambda$.

Since $d(X, l_2^n) \le \sqrt{n}$ for any $X \in \mathfrak{M}_n$, it follows that $s(X) \le \sqrt{n}$. The exact order of growth of the quantity $s_n = \sup\{s(X) : X \in \mathfrak{M}_n\}$ was computed by Mankiewicz [36].

THEOREM 2 [36]. $s_n \asymp n^{1/2}$.

The proof of this result is based on the following construction. Let $X, Y \in (\mathfrak{M}_n, \nu_{20n}, B_1^n)$ be independent random spaces, and define $Z = X \oplus_2 Y$ (i.e., Z is the space of pairs $z = (x, y)$, $x \in X$, $y \in Y$, equipped with the norm

$\|z\| = (\|x\|^2 + \|y\|^2)^{1/2})$. Computation of the expectation of the variable $s(Z)$ leads to the required result.

The Enflo example of a space without the approximation property gave rise to the following finite-dimensional problem: Does there exist a sequence of spaces $X_n \in \mathfrak{M}_n$ with basis constants increasing without limit? We recall the corresponding definitions. Associated with any basis $x_1, \ldots, x_n$ in X is the sequence of projections $P_1, \ldots, P_n$:

$$P_k \left(\sum \alpha_i x_i \right) = \sum_{i=1}^{k} \alpha_i x_i.$$

The basis constant of the system $x_1, \ldots, x_n$ is defined as

$$b(\{x_i\}_1^n) = \sup_{1 \leq k \leq n} \|P_k\|.$$

The infimum of the quantities $b(\{x_i\}_1^n)$ over all possible bases $\{x_i\}_1^n$ is called the *basis constant of X* and denoted by $b(X)$. It follows from John's theorem [27] that $b(X) \leq \sqrt{n}$.

It was proved in [20] that for each n there is a space $X \in \mathfrak{M}_n$ with the following property ($c > 0$ is an absolute constant)

$$\|P\| > c\frac{\min\{\operatorname{rank} P, n\text{-}\operatorname{rank} P\}}{\sqrt{n \log n}}, \quad \text{for any projection } P \text{ on } X. \quad (4)$$

In particular, $b(X) > 2^{-1}c\sqrt{n/\log n}$. What is more, we have the following result.

THEOREM 3 [20]. *Suppose that $X \in \mathfrak{M}_n$ is a random space with distribution $\nu_{n^2, n^{-1/2}B_2^n}$. In this case the probability of the event (4) tends to 1 as n increases.*

Using a slightly different probability construction, Szarek [53] proved independently the following result, which establishes the right order of size.

THEOREM 4 [53]. *For each n there exists an $X_n \in \mathfrak{M}_n$ such that $\|P\| \geq \delta n^{1/2}$ ($\delta > 0$ an absolute constant) for every projection P on X_n of rank $[n/2]$. In particular, $b(X_n) \geq \delta n^{1/2}$.*

By developing his construction, Szarek [54] was able to "glue together" from finite-dimensional spaces an infinite-dimensional Banach space without a basis and with the bounded approximation property, and to solve thereby one of the last problems generated by the Enflo example. (By a theorem of Pełczyński [42], the presence of the bounded approximation property for a Banach space means that it is isomorphic to a complemented subspace of a space with a basis.)

A classical result of Kadets and Snobar asserts that for each n-dimensional subspace L of a Banach space X there is a projection $P: X \to L$ such that $\|P\| \leq \sqrt{n}$. Theorem 4 proves the existence of an n-dimensional space

in which this estimate cannot be essentially improved in the case of subspaces of dimension $[n/2]$. The example of Theorem 3 leads to nontrivial
lower estimates of the norms of all projections with rank and corank greater
than $\sqrt{n \cdot \log n}$. However, it is not yet clear whether there is a sequence
of spaces $X_n \in \mathfrak{M}_n$ and a function φ increasing without limit such that
$\|P\| \geq \varphi(\text{rank } P)$ for every projection P on X_n of rank at most $\frac{n}{2} + 1$.

In the remarkable paper [44] Pisier constructed an example of an infinite-
dimensional Banach space having, in particular, the following property:
$\|P\| > c\sqrt{\text{rank } P}$ for every finite-dimensional projection P on it, where $c > 0$
is an absolute constant.

So far all considerations have been for real spaces. It is not complicated
to carry them over to the complex case. One must simply regard an n-
dimensional complex space as a $2n$-dimensional real space. For example, the
definition of the measures $\nu_{k,B}$ is simulated as follows. For $m = 1, \dots, k$
let $\xi_m, \eta_m \in \mathbf{R}^n$, and define $f_m = \xi_m + i\eta_m \in \mathbf{C}^n$. Further, let $B \subset \mathbf{C}^n$ be a
fixed absolutely convex subset of $\mathbf{C}^n$. Define the set $A_F^{\mathbf{C}}$ $(F = (f_1, \dots, f_k))$
by

$$A_F^{\mathbf{C}} = \left\{ z \in \mathbf{C}^n : \exists \lambda_0, \dots, \lambda_k \in \mathbf{C}, \sum_{m=0}^{k} |\lambda_m| \leq 1, z \in \lambda_0 B + \sum_{m=1}^{k} \lambda_m f_m \right\}$$

and let X_F be the n-dimensional (over the field $\mathbf{C}$) normed space with unit
ball $A_F^{\mathbf{C}}$. The measure $\nu_{k,B}^{\mathbf{C}}$ is induced under the mapping $F \to X_F$ when
ξ_m and η_m run independently through (S^{n-1}, μ_n).

In the "real" approach to complex spaces the question naturally arises as
to whether the complex structure is determined by the real geometry of the
space, in other words, whether there exist complex Banach spaces that are
not isomorphic in the complex sense but are isomorphic in the real sense.
To formulate the analogous question in the finite-dimensional case we introduce the following notation. Let X and Y be normed spaces that are
n-dimensional over the field of complex numbers. Let

$$d_{\mathbf{C}}(X, Y) = \inf \{\|T\| \|T^{-1}\| : T : X \to Y$$
$$\text{is a (complex-)linear invertible operator}\},$$

$$d_{\mathbf{R}}(X, Y) = \inf \{\|S\| \|S^{-1}\| : S : X \to Y$$
$$\text{is a real-linear invertible operator}\}.$$

QUESTION. Is it true that the equality $d_{\mathbf{R}}(X, Y) = 1$ implies that $d_{\mathbf{C}}(X, Y)$
$< K$ (K an absolute constant)?

Bourgain gave a negative answer to this question [7]. The following definitions are needed for an exact formulation of his result. Let X be a complex
Banach space. Denote by $\overline{X}$ the complex Banach space coinciding with X
as a set, with the product $\lambda \circ x$ of a scalar λ by an element $x \in \overline{X}$ defined
by the equality $\lambda \circ x = \bar{\lambda}x$ ($\bar{\lambda}$ is the complex conjugate of λ). The addition

operation and the norm in $\overline{X}$ are inherited from X (X and $\overline{X}$ are thereby isometric in the real sense).

Let the Banach space X be identified with a linear subspace of the space l_2 (or l_2^n). Denote by X_θ, $0 < \theta < 1$, the space $[X, l_2]_{\theta, 2}$ obtained by real interpolation (see, for example, [5] for the definition). Let $X_0 = X$ and $X_1 = l_2$ (or l_2^n).

THEOREM 5 [7]. *Let X^n be a complex n-dimensional random space with distributions $\nu_{n^4, \varnothing}^C$. Then with some absolute constant $\delta > 0$ the probability that $d_C(X_\theta^n, \overline{X}_\theta^n) > (\delta n / \log n)^{1-\theta}$ is positive and tends to 1 with increasing n for every $\theta \in [0, 1]$.*

Moreover, Bourgain was also able to show that with large probability the space X_θ^n cannot be "nicely" imbedded in $\overline{X}_\theta^n + l_2$, a fact that enabled him to "glue together" from them an infinite-dimensional Banach space Z not isomorphic to $\overline{Z}$.

Judging from the references, a result close to Theorem 5 was proved by Szarek [5]. Mankiewicz succeeded in discovering a general fact which yields assertions of the type of Theorems 2–5 as special cases, though with somewhat worse estimates (differing from the best estimates by a logarithmic factor).

In stating Theorems 1–5 we did not make precise the rate at which the measures of the corresponding sets tend to 1. In fact, exponential estimates for the measure of the complementary set are obtained in the proofs of these assertions. We do not dwell on this in detail, since for geometric applications the positivity of the measures is what is important: that is what yields the existence theorems.

2. Approximation by random subspaces

Let L be a linear subspace of a Banach space X, and B a subset of X. The *deviation* of the set B from L is defined to be the quantity

$$\rho(B, L) = \rho_X(B, L) = \sup_{x \in B} \inf_{y \in L} \|x - y\|.$$

The Kolmogorov widths of a set B are defined by

$$d_n(B, X) = \inf_{L_n : \dim L_n \leq n} \rho_X(B, L);$$

the infimum is over the set of all subspaces of dimension at most n. This concept was introduced in 1936 by Kolmogorov [34]. The question of the rate of decrease of the widths generalizes in a natural way the classical approximation theory problem of the degree of approximation of a function class by fixed finite-dimensional subspaces (algebraic or trigonometric polynomials, and so on). Historically, the problem of estimating the widths of the Sobolev classes W_p^l in L_q was the first to emerge in this area. The close connection between the problem of the widths $d_n(W_p^l, L_q)$ and the finite-dimensional question of a uniform estimate of $d_n(B_p^N, l_q^N)$ revealed itself already in the initial papers on this topic (Stechkin [48], Solomyak and Tikhomirov [46]). It is relatively uncomplicated to compute the exact values of the widths $d_n(B_p^N, l_q^N)$ for $1 \leq q \leq p \leq \infty$ (see, for example, [43] and [47]). However, obtaining even any kind of interesting estimate for $d_n(B_p^N, l_q^N)$ turns out to be difficult when $\max\{2, p\} < q \leq \infty$. It was only in 1974 that Ismagilov [26] was able to get an estimate of $d_n(B_1^N, l_\infty^N)$ that is substantive in a broad domain of variation of n and N, by using special subspaces invariant under a cyclic shift for approximating the "octahedron" B_1^N. Further, he introduced an important concept—the trigonometric width—which has received little study so far (the author knows of only two publications on this topic: Belinskiĭ [1], and Makovoz [35]).

A probabilistic way of arguing first used by Kashin in [30] and [32] to estimate widths has proved to be very fruitful in this circle of questions. The scheme of his arguments is as follows. One introduces a probability measure on the manifold of all n-dimensional subspaces of a space X. The mean value of the deviation $\rho_X(B, L)$ with respect to this measure is used to estimate the width $d_n(B, X)$. If the probability measure is chosen well, then this mean value is close to $B_n(B, X)$, and its computation can turn out to be considerably easier than a direct estimate of the width. In realizing this approach to estimate $d_n(B_2^N, l_\infty^N)$, Kashin introduced a measure on $G_{n, N}$ as follows. Let $A = (a_{ij})$ be a random $n \times N$ matrix whose elements take the values ± 1 independently with probability $1/2$. The needed measure on the manifold $G_{n, N}$ is induced upon passing from the matrix A to the n-dimensional subspace of $\mathbf{R}^N$ that is its range. Kashin succeeded in proving that

$$\rho_{l_\infty^N}(B_2^N, L) \leq c(\log(N/n) + 1)^{3/2}/\sqrt{n}$$

(c an absolute constant) with large probability for such a choice of the measure on $G_{n, N}$. As mentioned in the Introduction, this gives a sharp estimate on the power scale (and the exact order when $n \asymp N$) for the widths $d_n(B_2^N, l_\infty^N)$.

Kashin's arguments simplify if we pass to the unitarily invariant measure $\mu_{n, N}$ on the manifold $G_{n, N}$ of all n-dimensional subspaces of $\mathbf{R}^N$. It is also possible to get sharper estimates here. It is useful to bear in mind that the measure $\mu_{n, N}$ is induced (in passing from the matrix to its range) by a random $n \times N$ matrix $\Gamma = (g_{ij})$ with independent Gaussian random variables as elements.

THEOREM 6 ([21], [18]; see also [60]). *For $L \in G_{n, N}$ the inequalities*

$$\rho_{l_q^N}(B_2^N, L) \leq c \min\{1, N^{1/q}/\sqrt{n}\} \quad \text{for } q < \infty, \tag{5}$$

$$\rho_{l_\infty^N}(B_2^N, L) \leq c \min\{1, \sqrt{(\log(N/n) + 1)/n}\} \tag{6}$$

($c < \infty$ *an absolute constant*) *hold with positive* $\mu_{n,N}$-*probability* (*tending to* 1 *as* n *increases*).

These estimates give the right order for the corresponding widths (see [21] and [18]). With their help we can conclude the investigation of the question of the orders of the widths $d_n(B_p^N, l_q^N)$ for $1 \le p < q < \infty$ and $2 \le p < q = \infty$ by uncomplicated arguments of interpolation nature. The next result shows that the sets B_p^N with $1 \le p \le 2$ turn out to be indistinguishable from the point of view of approximation in l_∞^N by random subspaces. At the same time, the widths $d_n(B_1^N, l_\infty^N)$ and $d_n(B_2^N, l_\infty^N)$ have different order when $n = o(N)$, as shown by a well-known result of Kashin [31] (see also Höllig [25]). In other words, for $1 \le p < q < \infty$ or for $2 \le p < q = \infty$ a subspace of $(G_{n,N}, \mu_{n,N})$ in general position is almost extremal for the width $d_n(B_p^N, l_q^N)$, while for $1 \le p < 2 < q = \infty$ it is not.

THEOREM 7 [23]. *For* $L \in G_{n,N}$ *the inequalities*

$$c_1 \min\{1, \sqrt{(\log(N/n) + 1/n})\} \le \rho_{l_\infty^N}(B_p^N, L)$$

$$\le c_2 \min\{1, \sqrt{(\log(N/n) + 1)/n}\}$$

($0 < c_1 < c_2 < \infty$ *absolute constants*) *hold for every* p *with* $1 \le p \le 2$ *with positive* $\mu_{n,N}$-*probability* (*tending to* 1 *as* n *increases*).

Recently B. Carl (personal communication) reproved the main result

$$d_n(B_2^N, l_\infty^N) \ge c \min\{1, \sqrt{(\log(N/n) + 1)/n}\}$$

of [18] and proved the inequality

$$d_n(TB_2^N, l_\infty^N) \le c\|T\| \min\{1, \sqrt{(\log(N/n) + 1)/n}\},$$

where T is an arbitrary operator acting from l_2^N to l_∞^N.

It is convenient to prove the inequalities (5) and (6) in dual terms. This approach was employed by Mityagin [40] in a reworking of a result of Kashin in [32]. Let X and Y be N-dimensional Banach spaces, with X imbedded in a fixed way in Y, and let B be the unit ball of X. By using the Hahn-Banach theorem it is not hard to show (see, for example, [26]) that for every subspace $L \subset Y$

$$\rho_Y(B, L) = \sup\{\|z\|_{X^*}/\|z\|_{Y^*} : z \ne 0, z \in L^\perp\}.$$

Here and below, X^* and Y^* are the spaces dual to X and Y, and $L^\perp \subset Y^*$ is the subspace of functionals annihilating L. Let

$$K(\lambda) = \{z \in Y^* : \|z\|_{X^*} \le \lambda \|z\|_{Y^*}\}. \tag{7}$$

In this notation the assertion $d_n(B, Y) \le \lambda$ is equivalent to the condition that there is a subspace $L^n \subset Y^*$ of codimension at most n such that $L^n \cap K(\lambda) = 0$. Thus, the problem of estimating the widths reduces to the question of how small the codimension of a subspace not intersecting a given cone can be. The following simple assertion helps to answer this question.

PROPOSITION 2. *Suppose that* $f_1, \ldots, f_m \in B_2^N$, $m \leq 2^n$, *and the vector* $z \in \mathbf{R}^N$ *is such that* $\|z\|_2 > 12$. *If* $V = \operatorname{conv}\{f_1, \ldots, f_m\}$ *is a convex polytope with vertices* $f_1, \ldots, f_m$, *and*

$$K = \{z \in \mathbf{R}^N : x = \alpha(z + v), \alpha > 0, v \in V\}$$

is the conical hull of the set $z + V$, *then*

$$\mu_{n,N}\{L \in G_{n,N} : L^\perp \cap K \neq \varnothing\} \leq 2^{-n}.$$

PROOF. Recall first that the probability measure $\mu_{n,N}$ is induced under the mapping $\Gamma \to \operatorname{Im}\Gamma$ by the Gaussian measure $\gamma_{n,N}$ on the space of $n \times N$ matrices, identified in the standard way with $\mathbf{R}^{nN}$. If L is defined as $\operatorname{Im}\Gamma$, then the condition $L^\perp \cap K \neq \varnothing$ is equivalent to the condition that there be a $v \in V$ such that $v + z \in \ker\Gamma^*$ (Γ^* is the transposed matrix). In other words, $\Gamma^* v = -\Gamma^* z$. What is more, $\|\Gamma^* v\|_2 = \|\Gamma^* z\|_2$, and

$$\max_{1 \leq i \leq m} \|\Gamma^* f_i\|_2 \geq \|\Gamma^* z\|_2$$

by the definition of the set V. Since a sum of independent Gaussian random variables is again a Gaussian random variable, the vectors $\Gamma^* f_i / \|f_i\|_2$ and $\Gamma^* z / \|z\|_2$ have distribution γ_n. For our purposes the following estimates of the distribution of the norm of a Gaussian vector $g \in (\mathbf{R}^n, \gamma_n)$ suffice:

$$\gamma_n\{g : \|g\|_2^2 \geq 4n\} \leq 16^{-n},$$
$$\gamma_n\{g : \|g\|_2^2 \leq n/36\} \leq 2(2\sqrt{2})^{-n}.$$

It remains to observe that if $\max_{1 \leq i \leq m} \|\Gamma^* f_i\|_2 \geq \|\Gamma^* z\|_2$, then either

$$\max_{1 \leq i \leq m} \|\Gamma^* f_i\|_2 / \|f_i\|_2 \geq 2\sqrt{n}$$

or

$$\|\Gamma^* z\|_2 / \|z\|_2 < \sqrt{n}/6.$$

COROLLARY. *For* $i = 1, \ldots, 2^n - 1$ *let* $V_i \subset B_2^N$ *and* $z_i \in \mathbf{R}^N$ *be polytopes and elements as in Proposition 2, and let* $K_i = \operatorname{con}\{z_i + V_i\}$ *be the conical hull of the set* $z_i + V_i$. *Then there exists a subspace* $L^n \subset \mathbf{R}^n$ *of codimension* n *such that* $L^n \cap (\bigcup_{i=1}^{2^n-1} K_i) = \varnothing$.

To estimate the widths it thereby suffices to cover the cone $K(\lambda)$ in (7) by a "small" number of cones of a special form. This is the way Theorem 6 was proved.

In the formulation of Proposition 2 it was assumed that the set V is a polytope with a "small" number of vertices. This is very intuitive geometrically, but only the following property of such sets was used in the proof (as before, Γ is a Gaussian $n \times N$ matrix):

$$\gamma_{nN}\{\Gamma : \sup\{\|\Gamma^* x\|_2 : x \in V\} > 4\sqrt{n}\} \leq 8^{-n}.$$

The isoperimetric property of a Gaussian measure ([51] and [6]) shows that such an estimate holds if

$$h_1(V) \stackrel{\text{def}}{=} \int_{\mathbf{R}^n} \sup\{|\langle \xi, x \rangle| : x \in V\} \, d\gamma_n(\xi) \le c\sqrt{n}$$

($c > 0$ an absolute constant).

The question arises as to what intrinsic characteristics of the cone $\mathcal{K}$ enable one to construct a covering $\mathcal{K} = \bigcup_{i=1}^{2^n-1} \mathcal{K}_i$ of it such that $\mathcal{K}_i = \text{con}\{V_i + z_i\}$, where $\|z_i\|_2 > 12$, $V_i \subset B_2^N$, and $h_1(V_i) < c\sqrt{n}$. Pajor and Tomczak-Jaegermann succeeded in obtaining an answer, and that led them to the following elegant result.

THEOREM 8 [41]. *Let K be a cone in $\mathbf{R}^N$. There exists an absolute constant $c < \infty$ such that if $h_1(K \cap B_2^N) < c\sqrt{n}$ for some n, then*

$$\mu_{n,N}\{L \in G_{n,N} : L^\perp \cap K \ne \varnothing\} \le 2^{-n}.$$

The proof is based essentially on entropy estimates obtained by Sudakov [50] for Gaussian random processes.

The following simple assertion, which is a consequence of the isoperimetric property of a Gaussian measure, shows that to within a constant the condition $h_1(K \cap B_2^N) \le c\sqrt{n}$ is necessary for realization of the scheme.

PROPOSITION 3. *Let $A \subset \bigcup_{i \in I} A_i \subset B_2^N$. Then*

$$h_1(A) \le \max_{i \in I} h_1(A_i) + c\sqrt{\log \operatorname{Card} I},$$

where c is an absolute constant.

The following question is of interest.

Is it true that if a cone $K \subset \mathbf{R}^N$ is such that the $\mu_{n,N}$-measure of the subspaces $L \in G_{n,N}$ with $K \cap L^\perp \ne \varnothing$ is sufficiently small (for example, less than $1/2$ or $1/2^n$), then $h_1(K \cap B_2^N) \le c\sqrt{n}$ (c an absolute constant)?

In a certain very weak sense this is actually the case, as shown by the following elementary observation of the author and B. S. Tsirel'son. Suppose that the cone K and the subspace $L \in G_{n,N}$ are such that $K \cap L^\perp = \varnothing$. Then for every $\varepsilon > 0$ there is a linear transformation T such that $TK \cap B_2^N$ lies in the ε-neighborhood of some n-dimensional subspace. Consequently, $h_1(TK \cap B_2^N) \le c(\sqrt{n} + \varepsilon\sqrt{N})$ with some absolute constant c. In other words, the required result is obtained if one considers the form $\langle Tx, Ty \rangle$ with a suitable T instead of the usual inner product in $\mathbf{R}^N$.

BIBLIOGRAPHY

1. È. S. Belinskiĭ, *Approximation of periodic functions of several variables by a "floating" system of exponentials, and trigonometric widths*, Dokl. Akad. Nauk SSSR **284** (1985), 1294–1297; English transl. in Soviet Math. Dokl. **32** (1985).

2. G. Bennett, L. E. Dor, V. Goodman, W. B. Johnson, and C. M. Newman, *On uncomplemented subspaces of* L_p, $1 < p < 2$, Israel J. Math. **26** (1977), 178–187.

3. G. Bennett, V. Goodman, and C. M. Newman, *Norms of random matrices*, Pacific J. Math. **59** (1975), 359–365.

4. Y. Benyamini and Y. Gordon, *Random factorization of operators between Banach spaces*, J. Analyse Math. **39** (1981), 45–74.

5. Jöran Bergh and Jörgen Löfström, *Interpolation spaces: an introduction*, Springer-Verlag, 1976.

6. Christer Borell, *The Brunn-Minkowski inequality in Gauss space*, Invent. Math. **30** (1975), 207–216.

7. J. Bourgain, *A complex Banach space such that* X *and* $\overline{X}$ *are not isomorphic*, Preprint.

8. J. Bourgain and V. D. Milman, *On Mahler's conjecture on the volume of a convex symmetric body and its polar*, Preprint, Inst. Hautes Études Sci., Bures-sur-Yvette, 1984.

9. ___, *Distances between normed spaces, their subspaces and quotient spaces*, Preprint, Inst. Hautes Études Sci., Bures-sur-Yvette, 1984.

10. S. Chevet, *Séries de variables aléatoires gaussiennes à valeurs dans* $E \widehat{\otimes}_\varepsilon F$. *Application aux produits d'espaces de Wiener abstraits*, Séminaire Maurey-Schwartz sur la Géométrie des Espaces de Banach (1977/78), Exposé 19, École Polytech., Palaiseau, 1978.

11. A. M. Davie, *The approximation problem for Banach spaces*, Bull. London Math. Soc. **5** (1973), 261–266.

12. W. J. Davis, V. D. Milman, and N. Tomczak-Jaegermann, *The distance between certain n-dimensional Banach spaces*, Israel J. Math. **39** (1981), 1–15.

13. Per Enflo, *A counterexample to the approximation problem in Banach spaces*, Acta Math. **130** (1973), 309–317.

14. T. Figiel, *A short proof of Dvoretzky's theorem on almost spherical sections of convex bodies*, Compositio Math. **33** (1976), 297–301.

15. T. Figiel and W. B. Johnson, *Large subspaces of* l_∞^n *and estimates of the Gordon-Lewis constant*, Israel J. Math. **37** (1980), 92–112.

16. Tadeusz Figiel, Stanisław Kwapień, and Aleksander Pełczyński, *Sharp estimates for the constants of local unconditional structure of Minkowski spaces*, Bull. Acad. Polon. Sci. Sér. Sci. Math. Astr. Phys. **25** (1977), 1221–1226.

17. T. Figiel, J. Lindenstrauss, and V. D. Milman, *The dimension of almost spherical sections of convex bodies*, Acta Math. **139** (1977), 53–94.

18. A. Yu. Garnaev and E. D. Gluskin, *On widths of the Euclidean ball*, Dokl. Akad. Nauk SSSR **277** (1984), 1048–1052; English transl. in Soviet Math. Dokl. **30** (1984).

19. E. D. Gluskin, *The diameter of the Minkowski compactum is roughly equal to* n, Funktsional. Anal. i Prilozhen. **15** (1981), no. 1, 72–73; English transl. in Functional Anal. Appl. **15** (1981).

20. ___, *Finite-dimensional analogues of spaces without a basis*, Dokl. Akad. Nauk SSSR **261** (1981), 1046–1050; English transl. in Soviet Math. Dokl. **24** (1981).

21. ___, *Norms of random matrices and widths of finite-dimensional sets*, Mat. Sb. **120 (162)** (1983), 180–189; English transl. in Math. USSR Sb. **48** (1984).

22. ___, *On some finite-dimensional problems in the theory of widths*, Vestnik Leningrad. Univ. **1981**, no. 13 (Ser. Mat. Mekh. Astr. vyp. 3), 5–10; English transl. in Vestnik Leningrad Univ. Math. **14** (1982).

23. ___, *An octahedron is poorly approximated by random subspaces*, Funktsional Anal. i Prilozhen. **20** (1986), no. 1, 14–20; English transl. in Functional Anal. Appl. **20** (1986).

24. Y. Gordon, *Asymmetry and projection constants of Banach spaces*, Israel J. Math. **14** (1973), 50–62.

25. Klaus Höllig, *Approximationszahlen von Sobolev-Einbettungen*, Math. Ann. **242** (1979), 273–281.

26. R. S. Ismagilov, *Widths of sets in normed linear spaces and approximation of functions by trigonometric polynomials*, Uspekhi Mat. Nauk **29** (1974), no. 3 (177), 161–178; English transl. in Russian Math. Surveys **29** (1974).

27. Fritz John, *Extremum problems with inequalities as subsidiary conditions*, Studies and Essays Presented to R. Courant on his 60th Birthday, Interscience, 1948, pp. 187–204.

28. William B. Johnson and Gideon Schechtman, *Embedding l_p^m into l_1^n*, Acta Math. **149** (1982), 71–85.

29. M. I. Kadets, *On the linear dimension of the spaces L_p and l_q*, Uspekhi Mat. Nauk **13** (1958), no. 6 (84), 95–98. (Russian)

30. B. S. Kashin, *On the Kolmogorov widths of octahedra*, Dokl. Akad. Nauk SSSR **214** (1974), 1024–1026; English transl. in Soviet Math. Dokl. **15** (1974).

31. ___, *On widths of octahedra*, Uspekhi Mat. Nauk **30** (1975), no. 4 (184), 251–252. (Russian)

32. ___, *Widths of certain finite-dimensional sets and classes of smooth functions*, Izv. Akad. Nauk SSSR Ser. Mat. **41** (1977), 334–351; English transl. in Math. USSR Izv. **11** (1977).

33. S. V. Kisliakov [Kislyakov], *What is needed for a 0-absolutely summing operator to be nuclear?*, Complex Analysis and Spectral Theory (Leningrad, 1979/80), Lecture Notes in Math., vol. 864, Springer-Verlag, 1981, pp. 336–364.

34. A. Kolmogoroff [A. N. Kolmogorov], *Über die beste Annäherung von Funktionen einer gegebenen Funktionenklasse*, Ann. of Math. (2) **37** (1936), 107–110.

35. Y. Makovoz, *On trigonometric n-widths and their generalization*, J. Approximation Theory **41** (1984), 361–366.

36. P. Mankiewicz, *Finite-dimensional Banach spaces with symmetry constant of order $\sqrt{n}$*, Studia Math. **79** (1984), 193–200.

37. ___, *Subspace mixing properties of operators in $\mathbf{R}^n$ with applications to Gluskin spaces*, Studia Math. **88** (1988), 51–67.

38. V. D. Mil'man, *A new proof of Dvoretzky's theorem on sections of convex bodies*, Funktsional. Anal. i Prilozhen. **5** (1971), no. 4, 28–37; English transl. in Functional Anal. Appl. **5** (1971).

39. B. S. Mityagin, *Banach function spaces of Enflo type*, Proc. Sixth Winter School Math. Programming and Related Questions (Drogobych, 1973): Functional Anal. and Appl., Tsentral Èkonom.-Mat. Inst. Akad. Nauk SSSR, Moscow, 1975, pp. 7–27. (Russian)

40. ___, *Random matrices and subspaces*, Geometry of Linear Spaces and Operator Theory, (B. S. Mityagin, editor), Yaroslav. Gos. Univ., Yaroslavl', 1977, pp. 175–202. (Russian)

41. Alain Pajor and Nicole Tomczak-Jaegermann, *Subspaces of small codimension of finite-dimensional Banach spaces*, Proc. Amer. Math. Soc. **97** (1986), 637–642.

42. A. Pełczyński, *Any separable Banach space with the bounded approximation property is a complemented subspace of a Banach space with a basis*, Studia Math. **40** (1971), 239–243.

43. Albrecht Pietsch, *s-numbers of operators in Banach spaces*, Studia Math. **51** (1974), 201–223.

44. Gilles Pisier, *Counterexamples to a conjecture of Grothendieck*, Acta Math. **151** (1983), 181–208.

45. ___, *On the dimension of the l_p^n-subspaces of Banach spaces, for $1 \leq p < 2$*, Trans. Amer. Math. Soc. **276** (1983), 201–211.

46. M. Z. Solomyak and V. M. Tikhomirov, *On the geometric characteristics of the imbedding of W_p^α in C*, Izv. Vyssh. Uchebn. Zaved. Mat. **1967**, no. 10 (65), 76–82. (Russian)

47. M. I. Stesin, *The Aleksandrov widths of finite-dimensional sets and classes of smooth functions*, Dokl. Akad. Nauk SSSR **220** (1975), 1278–1281; English transl. in Soviet Math. Dokl. **16** (1975).

48. S. B. Stechkin, *On the best approximation of given function classes by arbitrary polynomials*, Uspekhi Mat. Nauk **9** (1954), no. 1 (59), 133–134. (Russian)

49. Walter Stromquist, *The maximum distance between two-dimensional Banach spaces*, Math. Scand. **48** (1981), 205–225.

50. V. N. Sudakov, *Gaussian random processes and measures of solid angles in a Hilbert space*, Dokl. Akad. Nauk SSSR **197** (1971), 43–45; English transl. in Soviet Math. Dokl. **12** (1971).

51. V. N. Sudakov and B. S. Tsirel'son, *Extremal properties of half-spaces for spherically invariant measures*, Zap. Nauchn. Sem. Leningrad. Otdel. Mat. Inst. Steklov. (LOMI) **41** (1974), 14–24; English transl. in J. Soviet Math. **9** (1978), no. 1.

52. Andrzej Szankowski, *On Dvoretzky's theorem on almost spherical sections of convex bodies*, Israel J. Math. **17** (1974), 325–338.

53. Stanisław J. Szarek, *The finite-dimensional basis problem with an appendix on nets of Grassmann manifolds*, Acta Math. **151** (1983), 153–179.

54. ___, *A Banach space without a basis which has the bounded approximation property*, Acta Math. **159** (1987), 81–98.

55. ___, *On the existence and uniqueness of complex structure and spaces with "few" operators*, Trans. Amer. Math. Soc. **293** (1986), 339–353.

56. ___, *On Kashin's almost Euclidean orthogonal decomposition of l_1^n*, Bull. Acad. Polon. Sci. Sér. Sci. Math. Astr. Phys. **26** (1978), 691–694.

57. Stanisław Szarek and Nicole Tomczak-Jaegermann, *On nearly Euclidean decomposition for some classes of Banach spaces*, Compositio Math. **40** (1980), 367–385.

58. Nicole Tomczak-Jaegermann, *The Banach-Mazur distance between the trace classes c_p^n*, Proc. Amer. Math. Soc. **72** (1978), 305–308.

59. ___, *The Banach-Mazur distance between symmetric spaces*, Israel J. Math. **46** (1983), 40–66.

60. ___, *On n-widths of finite-dimensional spaces*, preprint.

Leningrad Institute of Economics and Finance
Leningrad 191023
USSR

Translated by H. H. McFADEN

Amer. Math. Soc. Transl.
(2) Vol. **147**, 1990

Homeomorphisms of the Circle, Modifications of Functions, and Fourier Series

A. M. OLEVSKIĬ

We consider Fourier series of continuous functions defined on the circle $T = \mathbf{R}/2\pi\mathbf{Z}$:

$$f \sim \sum_{n \in \mathbf{Z}} \hat{f}(n)e^{int}. \tag{1}$$

The topic of our report concerns how the basic properties of the expansions (1) such as uniform convergence of the series or summability of the Fourier transform are related to the topological and metric structure of the function, and to what extent these properties can be improved by transformations that preserve this structure or change it only slightly. In the role of such transformations we consider:

homeomorphisms of the circle onto itself (it is important to distinguish among them the absolutely continuous and singular homeomorphisms); and

so-called "corrections", i.e., changes in the values of the function on arbitrary sets of small Lebesgue measure.

According to a theorem of Pál (1914), improved by Bohr (1935), for each real function $f \in C(T)$ there is a homeomorphism $\varphi : T \to T$ such that the composition $F = f \circ \varphi$ has a uniformly convergent expansion (1). The method of proof enables one simultaneously to achieve a sufficiently rapid decrease of the Fourier coefficients, in particular, to achieve the condition

$$\hat{F} \in l_p(\mathbf{Z}) \qquad \forall p > 1. \tag{2}$$

For a long time the situation remained unclear for $p = 1$. Can an arbitrary real function $f \in C(T)$ be brought by a suitable change of variable into the

1980 *Mathematics Subject Classification* (1985 *Revision*). Primary 42-02, 42C10, 42A20, 42A24, 42A61, 42A28; Secondary 43A46, 42C20.

Translation of Proc. Internat. Congr. Math. (Berkeley, 1986), Vol. 2, Amer. Math. Soc., Providence, R. I., 1987, pp. 976–989; MR **89f**: 42006.

algebra $A(T)$ of absolutely convergent Fourier series? This problem, posed by Luzin, has significantly stimulated investigations on this topic in recent years.

An important role in the correction problem is played by a theorem of Men'shov (1940) strengthening the classical Luzin C-property. According to this theorem, for each function $f \in C(T)$ there is a function F with uniformly convergent Fourier series that differs from f on a set whose measure is less than a previously specified positive number ε.

The question of whether it is possible in a similar way to achieve the condition (2) for some $p < 2$, or, as one says, to remove the Carleman singularity, also remained open for a long time.

Below is a survey of results of the author that include, in particular, solutions of both the problems posed above, as well as a survey of work of others on related questions. We mention some unsolved problems (of various degrees of difficulty). In the last section we touch on some aspects of general orthogonal expansions.

1. The spaces U and A_p

1. Denote by $U(T)$ the Banach space of functions representable by uniformly convergent series (1), with the norm

$$\|f\| = \sup_\nu \left\| \sum_{|n|<\nu} \hat{f}(n)e^{int} \right\|_{C(T)}.$$

Let $A_p(T)$ be the Fourier transform of the space $l_p(\mathbf{Z})$, with the norm

$$\|f\| = \|\hat{f}\|_{l_p}.$$

Arising in the framework of harmonic analysis, these spaces are of interest from various points of view. In particular, A_1 $(= A)$ is a model example first used to give meaning to some ideas in the theory of Banach algebras. Stochastic methods have been employed with success in the study of these spaces; certain properties reveal an arithmetic nature.

A classical aspect of Fourier series consists in investigating metric and differentiability properties of a function that ensure that the function is in the spaces under consideration. For example, the Hausdorff-Young theorem, $L^q \subset A_{q/(q-1)}$, $1 \le q \le 2$, shows how the degree of summability of a Fourier transform increases as q increases. For $q > 2$ there is no similar effect: even a continuous function need not belong to any of the classes A_p with $p < 2$. In such cases f is said to have a *Carleman singularity*. Going along the Hölder scale $H^\alpha(T)$ leads to a further improvement in the rate of decrease of the Fourier transform:

$$H^\alpha \subset A_p, \qquad \alpha > \alpha(p) = 1/p - 1/2, \tag{3}$$

and, moreover, the result is definitive in that, for each p with $1 \leq p < 2$, the class A_p no longer entirely contains the Hölder class with *critical exponent* $\alpha(p)$ (Bernstein, Szász). Membership in $U(T)$ requires less smoothness; a corresponding best possible condition can be expressed in terms of the modulus of smoothness, namely, $\omega_f(\delta) = o(\ln 1/\delta)^{-1}$; it is closely connected with the logarithmic growth of the Lebesgue constants.

2. Smoothness conditions, however, capture only the "surface layer" of the spaces U and A_p. Their more subtle properties are determined by functions with slowly decreasing moduli of continuity. Typical from this point of view is the instability with respect to a smooth change of variable. According to the Beurling, Helson, and Leĭbenzon theorem, the homeomorphisms of the circle acting invariantly in the algebra $A(T)$ reduce to a rotation and a symmetry. It seems likely that such a result holds also for U. The first examples in this direction were indicated by Turán. Later results are due to Clunie and Alpár. The latter, in particular, proved [1] that for every nonlinear analytic diffeomorphism φ of the circle there is a function $f \in U$, $\omega_f(\delta) = O(\ln 1/\delta)^{-\alpha}$, such that $f \circ \varphi \notin U$. In respect to A it seems to be unknown whether it is possible to adjoin a corresponding smoothness estimate to the three-author theorem cited above; for example, is it true that for every nonlinear homeomorphism φ there is an $f \in A \cap H^{1/2}$ such that $f \circ \varphi \notin A$? We are also unaware of whether the question of homeomorphisms acting in A_p with $p > 1$ has been considered.

We mention also the following theorem of Kaufman (1974) (see [11]), proved earlier in the analytic case by Alpár: let φ be a homeomorphism of class C^ν, $\nu \geq 3$, with the derivatives $\varphi^{(k)}$, $2 \leq k \leq \nu$, not vanishing simultaneously. Then φ carries $A(T)$ into $U(T)$.

3. The space U, in contrast to A, does not form an algebra with respect to pointwise multiplication (Salem). The question arises as to what supply of functions one gets by starting from U and using finitely many operations of multiplication and addition. In other words, what is the algebra generated by U? The answer is given by

THEOREM 1 [25]. *The algebra of functions generated by $U(T)$ coincides with the algebra of all continuous functions on the circle. More precisely, each $f \in C(T)$ can be represented in the form*

$$f = \varphi_1 \cdot \varphi_2 + \varphi_3, \qquad \varphi_i \in U(T), \quad 1 \leq i \leq 3. \tag{4}$$

Further, the spectrum of harmonics in the expansion (1) *of the factors φ_1 and φ_2 can be concentrated on the positive and negative semiaxes, respectively. If f runs through a given compact subset of $C(T)$, then the φ_1 in* (4) *can be chosen to be universal.*

Comparison of two classical facts can serve as a heuristic consideration (which does not, however, provide any hints at the proof): the product of two convergent series is Cesàro summable, and the Fourier series of each continuous function is summable by this method. It has not been excluded that each $f \in C(T)$ can be factored in the form $f = \varphi_1 \cdot \varphi_2$, $\varphi_i \in U$.

2. Nonremovable singularities

The results given below show that singularities of Carleman type in general position reveal stability with respect to an arbitrary variation of the function preserving its values on some set of positive Lebesgue measure. In this respect the classes A_p, $p < 2$, differ fundamentally from U.

1. Men′shov's theorem led to the following question (see [27]): Does there exist for every continuous function f a function F differing from f on a set of small measure and belonging to the class $A_p(T)$ for some $p < 2$? Even the case $p = 1$ remained unclear, although Ul′yanov conjectured that the answer is no in this case. The proof was obtained 10 years later by different methods in [13] and [22]. The first publication was by Katznelson [13], who constructed an example of a function $f \in C(T)$ that could not be corrected into $A(T)$.[1] His method, based on properties of a so-called Rudin-Shapiro measure, was specific and not applicable for $p > 1$; as noted in [13], the function f constructed there has only a logarithmic modulus of continuity.
  Our approach enabled us to get stronger results.

THEOREM 2 ([22]; see [24] for details). *For each* p *with* $1 \le p < 2$ *there exists a function* f *with the critical exponent of smoothness, namely,* $f \in H^{\alpha(p)}$, *that cannot be brought into the class* $A_p(T)$ *by correcting it on a set not of full measure.*

Here it turns out that the effect of not being correctable is typical. Roughly speaking, the class A_p is too small for an arbitrary continuous or even Hölder function to be "corrected" into it.
  We clarify the method of proof in the relatively simpler case $p = 1$. Let us consider a discrete variant of the correction problem. Suppose that an arbitrary orthonormal basis $\{\tau_\nu\}$ is fixed in $\mathbf{C}^n$ along with the canonical basis $\{e_k\}$, and consider the cube $Q = \{x; |(x, e_k)| \le 1/n \ \forall k\}$ (which plays the role of the unit ball in $H^{1/2}(T)$). Obviously, $\sum_\nu |(x, \tau_\nu)| \le 1$ $(x \in Q)$. It turns out that for most vectors in the cube this estimate cannot be essentially improved by arbitrarily changing a fixed fraction of the coordinates (x, e_k). More precisely, for given positive numbers θ and h a vector $x \in Q$ is put in the set $X(n, \theta, h)$ if there is a vector $\tilde{x} \in \mathbf{C}^n$ such that

$$\sum_\nu |(\tilde{x}, \tau_\nu)| > h,$$

---

[1]"Corrected into $A(T)$" means modified on a set of arbitrarily small measure in such a way that the new function is in $A(T)$.

and

$$\text{card}\{k \, ; \, (x - \tilde{x}, e_k) = 0\} > \theta n. \tag{5}$$

It can be shown that for each θ and sufficiently small $h(\theta)$ the volume of the set $X(n, \theta, h(\theta))$ in the underlying real space $\mathbf{R}^{2n}$ is exponentially small with respect to the parameter n.

The transition from the discrete problem to the original problem is realized on the basis of the connection between the Fourier transforms on the circle group and on a discrete subgroup of it. The characters on the latter appear in the role of the τ_ν.

Variation of p leads to the following result.

THEOREM 3 ([22], [24]). *There exists a function $f \in C(T)$ with the property that each function $F \in C(T)$ coinciding with it on some set of positive measure has a Carleman singularity.*

The function f can be chosen from an arbitrary compact subset of H^ω with a specified majorant $\omega(\delta)$ of the modulus of continuity having order of decrease to 0 slower than every power.

It can be deduced by standard devices from the method of proof that the set of functions f in Theorem 3 is topologically massive: its complement is a countable union of nowhere dense sets.

2. This theme was later developed by Khrushchev in [30], a result of which relates to the case $p = 1$. Using the method in [22], he showed that the sample paths of certain random processes that are natural from a probabilistic point of view are almost surely not correctable into the class $A(T)$. However, the smoothness of these sample paths is somewhat inferior to the condition $f \in H^{1/2}$ of Theorem 2.

We remark also that Theorem 2, while definitive in the sense of Hölder smoothness, leaves the possibility of a certain refinement in the more detailed scale of classes H^ω. A question that remains open is whether each class H^ω not imbedded in $A(T)$ contains a function not correctable.

3. The finite-dimensional variant indicated above for the correction problem led to the following statement of the question. As before, let $\{e_k\}$ be the canonical basis, and $\{\tau_\nu\}$ an arbitrary different orthonormal basis in $\mathbf{C}^n$. We introduce analogues of the norms in C and U:

$$\|x\|_C = \max_k |(x, e_k)| \, ; \qquad \|x\|_U = \max_q \left\| \sum_{\nu < q} (x, \tau_\nu) \tau_\nu \right\|_C .$$

Does there exist for every $x \in \mathbf{C}^n$ and every θ with $0 < \theta < 1$ a "corrected" vector $\tilde{x}$ with the condition (5) such that $\|\tilde{x}\|_U \le K(\theta) \|x\|_C$? In the case of a discrete trigonometric system $\{\tau_\nu\}$ a positive answer to this question was given by Kashin [14], who used the method of a random arrangement of signs. The general case remains open.

4. We mention one more unsolved problem relating to this circle of questions. The author proved (1961) that there exists a function $f \in C(T)$ whose Fourier series (1) diverges almost everywhere after some rearrangement of terms. This theorem has a long history: it was formulated with the condition $f \in L^2$ by Kolmogorov as far back as 1926 (see [21], Chapter 3, for details). It follows from the general theory of orthogonal series that $\hat{f}$ cannot lie in L_p if $p < 2$. We are thus dealing with a singularity stronger than a Carleman singularity. Is it removable, i.e., can each function be corrected on a set of small measure in such a way that the Fourier series of the resulting function converges almost everywhere for every rearrangement? A positive answer seems most likely.

3. Extension from compact sets of measure zero

In contrast to the foregoing, in this section we consider the situation when the values of the function must not be changed on a specified compact set $E \subset T$. We are concerned with the possibility of interpolating an arbitrary function $f \in C(E)$ into the class $U(T)$ or $A_p(T)$, $p < 2$. It is well known that in both cases a positive answer requires that E have measure 0. Denote by $B(E)$ the restriction of a given function space $B(T)$ to the compact set E.

1. In the case of $A(T)$ there can arise obstacles of an arithmetic nature even for countable compact sets. A compact set E is called a *Helson set* if $A(E) = C(E)$. Duality considerations give an equivalent formulation in terms of Fourier transforms of measures concentrated on E. Helson sets have been thoroughly studied (see, for example, [10]). There is no effective characterization of them. It is known that the property of being a Helson set is connected with rational independence.

An analogous concept has been introduced also on the k-dimensional torus T^k. Here interesting connections with geometric characteristics of sets emerge. For example, McGehee and Woodward proved [19] that each convex curve in T^2 is not a Helson sequence; at the same time, the graph of a Lipschitz function can be a Helson set.

2. Continuity should be required in addition in the case of interpolation in A_p, $p > 1$. The corresponding Banach space $A_p^c(T)$ arises as the intersection of $A_p(T)$ and $C(T)$, with norm equal to the maximum of the two norms. Here duality considerations are even less effective, because the space dual to A_p^c has not been explicitly described. A compact set $E \subset T^k$ is called a *p-Helson set* if $A_p^c(E) = C(E)$. It is easy to show that every countable compact set is a p-Helson set for every $p > 1$. This is no longer the case for compact sets of measure zero. What is more, we have

THEOREM 4 [21]. *For every continuous function $f \notin A_p(T)$ ($p < 2$ fixed) there is a compact set E of measure zero such that the restriction $f|_E$ does not belong to $A_p^c(E)$.*

This means that Carleman singularities are *always* predetermined by the values of the function on certain compact sets of measure zero.

In these questions it is natural to invoke metric characteristics subtler than Lebesgue measure, for example, Hausdorff dimension. We present a result in this direction recently obtained by V. N. Demenko.

THEOREM 5. *If a compact set $E \subset T^k$ has Hausdorff dimension λ, then E is a p-Helson set for $p > p_0 = 2k/(2k - \lambda)$. There is a counterexample for $p < p_0$.*

3. The analogous problem for $U(T)$ (see [21], p.79) was completely solved by Oberlin.

THEOREM 6 [20]. $U(E) = C(E)$ *for every compact set $E \subset T$ of measure zero.*

It is interesting, and perhaps unexpected, that this result was obtained as a corollary to the Carleson theorem on convergence almost everywhere of L^2 Fourier series. The possibility of using this theorem in the study of the space U was discovered by Vinogradov [5], who showed that the Carleson-Hunt inequality (boundedness of the majorant operator of the partial sums) led to a nontrivial lower estimate of the norm of the functional $\Phi : f \to \int_T f \, d\mu$ on U:

$$\|\Phi\|_{U^*} \geq K \sup_{s>0} \text{meas}\{y ; (G\mu)(y) > s\}; \tag{6}$$

here $G\mu$ is the Cauchy-Stieltjes transform of the measure μ, and $K > 0$ is an absolute constant. This inequality, together with the asymptotic behavior of the Cauchy transforms of singular measures (Boole, Tsereteli, and others), leads to Theorem 6. Vinogradov and Khrushchev gave a detailed survey on this topic containing a number of additional results [6].

The question of the possibility of a constructive proof of Oberlin's theorem remains open. It would be interesting at least to single out fairly broad classes of compact sets for which an explicit construction of an interpolating operator can be determined. In this connection we mention the following proposition (Kahane and Katznelson; see [11]): if E is the Cantor set on the circle, then each $f \in C(E)$ falls in $U(T)$ after linear interpolation on the complementary open intervals.

Of other applications of inequality (6) we mention a result of Kislyakov giving a sharp estimate of the norm of the "correction" operator in the Men'shov sense.

THEOREM 7 [15]. *For every function $f \in C(T)$ and every $\varepsilon > 0$ there exists a function F, differing from f on a set of measure $< \varepsilon$, such that $\|F\|_U \leq K \ln(1/\varepsilon) \|f\|_{C(T)}$.*

The Men'shov method gives an estimate that is not best possible, namely, $\|F\|_U \leq K(1/\varepsilon)\|f\|_C$; but, on the other hand, it provides a transparent construction of a correcting operator (see [2], [21], and [30]).

4. Homeomorphisms of the circle, and the algebra $A(T)$

1. The Pál-Bohr theorem given in the Introduction shows that membership of a real continuous function f in U or A_p, $p > 1$, does not impose restrictions on it from a topological point of view. The analogous problem for $p = 1$ was posed by Luzin (see [2], Chapter IV, §12). The author obtained a solution in [23]. There turned out to be a topological invariant able to distinguish between the classes $C(T)$ and $A(T)$. It takes into account the character of oscillation of a function in left and right half-neighborhoods of a point. The basic role is played by the fact that *if F is a high-frequency pulse of unit amplitude for $t > 0$ that vanishes for $t < 0$, then $\|F\|_{A(T)}$ is necessarily large, and a lower estimate for this norm depends only on the frequency.* The exact formula is as follows (see [24], Lemma 3.3): suppose that in some γ-neighborhood of zero F has the form

$$F(t) = \begin{cases} \sin Ng(t), & 0 \leq t < \gamma, \\ 0, & -\gamma < t < 0, \end{cases}$$

where g is an arbitrary strictly increasing function on $[0, \gamma]$, $g(0) = 0$, and $g(\gamma) = \pi$. Then

$$\|F\|_{A(T)} > K \ln^\alpha N, \tag{7}$$

where K and α are absolute positive constants.

It is worth mentioning that if the behavior at zero takes place in a damped oscillation mode, then the effect is lost. It is clear, for example, that the function $F_N(t) = a(t)\sin Nt$, where $a(t)$ is the indicator function of the interval $[\delta, \pi - \delta]$ and is linearly interpolated on $[0, \delta]$ and $[\pi - \delta, \pi]$, satisfies the estimate $\|F_N\|_{A(T)} < K(\delta)$.

We remark that lower estimates for the quantity $\|e^{iNg}\|_A$ arise in the study of automorphisms of the algebra $A(T)$; in particular, for smooth nonlinear functions g they are based on a lemma of van der Corput. However, in contrast to (7), these estimates bear an asymptotic character with respect to N for a fixed g; but it is uniformity with respect to g that is needed. An important role in the proof of (7) is played by the analogy with Cohen's method for estimating the L_1-norms of exponential sums [16].

The inequality (7) leads to a theorem solving Luzin's problem.

THEOREM 8 ([23]; see [24] for details). *There exists a real function $f \in C(T)$ with the property that the composition $F = f \circ \varphi$ of it with an arbitrary homeomorphism φ of T onto itself does not belong to the algebra $A(T)$.*

The function f that we construct has modulus of continuity of order $O(\ln 1/\delta)^{-\alpha}$. It is unknown how close this smoothness is to the maximal possible smoothness; in particular, it is not excluded that Hölder functions can be brought into $A(T)$ by a suitable substitution.

2. In parallel with our paper [23], Kahane and Katznelson [12] worked out another approach to the Luzin problem that, however, leads only to the following result: there exists a pair of real functions f_1 and f_2 that cannot be brought into $A(T)$ simultaneously by a single change of variable. This approach is based on the following considerations: "bad" functions can be brought into $A(T)$ only by means of very nonsmooth substitutions; however, such substitutions take "good" functions out of this space (see [11] and [24] for details).

It is interesting that this result (and the considerations leading to it) are preserved under small perturbations of the class $A(T)$. For a given numerical sequence $\varepsilon(n)$, $n \in \mathbf{Z}$, we define the function class

$$A_\varepsilon = \left\{ F \, ; \, \sum |\widehat{F}(n)\varepsilon(n)| < \infty \right\}.$$

THEOREM 9 (Kahane and Katznelson; see [11] and [24]). *There exist a sequence* $\varepsilon(n) \to 0$ ($|n| \to \infty$) *and a pair of real functions* f_1, $f_2 \in C(T)$ *that cannot be brought into the class* A_ε *by a single homeomorphism* φ.

At the same time, Theorem 8 is definitive from this point of view and does not admit a similar strengthening. This follows from a result due to Saakyan:

THEOREM 10 [26]. *For each sequence* $\{\alpha(n)\} \notin l_1(\mathbf{N})$ (*under minimal regularity conditions*) *and for each real function* $f \in C(T)$ *there exists a homeomorphism* φ *such that* $F = f \circ \varphi$ *satisfies the condition* $\widehat{F}(n) = O(\alpha(|n|))$.

As for the class U, not only each pair of functions but even each compact subset of $C(T)$ can simultaneously be brought into it.

THEOREM 11 (Kahane and Katznelson, 1978; see [11]). *For each modulus of continuity* ω *there is a homeomorphism* φ *of the circle such that* $f \circ \varphi \in U$ *for all* $f \in H^\omega$.

The last two theorems are based on conceptually close considerations reminiscent of Men'shov's correction method.

It would be interesting to determine whether in Theorem 11 it is possible to achieve the coefficient condition $\widehat{f \circ \varphi}(n) = o(1/|n|)$ ensuring membership in the space $U(T)$.

5. The role of singular homeomorphisms

A change of variable erases the boundary distinguishing a function of class $A_p^c(T)$, $p > 1$, from an arbitrary continuous function. It turns out, however, that this effect bears a purely topological character. The metric structure of a function under the action of an "improving" homeomorphism in general position is inevitably distorted.

A homeomorphism φ is said to be *singular* if it carries some set of full measure into a set of measure zero.

THEOREM 12 [24]. 1. *For each $p \in [1, 2[$ there is a function f in the Hölder class with critical exponent $\alpha(p)$ in (3) such that if $f \circ \varphi \in A_p(T)$, then the homeomorphism φ is singular.*

2. *There exists a function $f \in C(T)$ whose composition with an arbitrary nonsingular homeomorphism has a Carleman singularity.*

This result is conceptually close to the theorems in §2; the proof is based on an appropriate modification of the method used there. A synthesis of the results mentioned can be realized. We say that functions f and g on the circle are *conjugate* if there exist compact sets F, $G \subset T$ of positive measure and a nonsingular homeomorphism $\varphi : F \to G$ such that $f|_F = g \circ \varphi$.

THEOREM 13. 1. *For each $p \in [1, 2[$ there exists a function $f \in H^{\alpha(p)}(T)$ that is not conjugate to any of the functions in the class $A_p(T)$.*

2. *There exists an $f \in C(T)$ such that each function conjugate to it has a Carleman singularity.*

It remains an open question (also mentioned by Luzin; see [2]) as to whether an arbitrary $f \in C(T)$ can be brought into $U(T)$ by an absolutely continuous homeomorphism. A positive answer seems most likely.

6. Invariant subsets

It is of interest to describe the invariant parts of the function classes under consideration, i.e., the collections of elements remaining in a given class under the action of an arbitrary homeomorphism of the circle. In other words, we are concerned with best possible conditions for membership of a function in a given class, expressed in topologically invariant terms. For U this problem was solved by Baernstein and Waterman [3] in terms of harmonic variation. It is easy to show that the invariant part of the algebra $A(T)$ is trivial: it consists of constants. The problem is unsolved for the classes A_p or A_p^c with $p > 1$.

Similar questions can have substance also for other function classes and for other transformation groups. In particular, Tsereteli [31] has studied "rearrangements" of functions, i.e., unitary operators corresponding to invertible measure-preserving mappings of the circle onto itself. One of his results is that the invariant part of the class $\operatorname{Re} H^1(T)$ (H^1 is the Hardy class) with respect to the indicated group of operators coincides with the class $L \ln^+ L$. An interesting metric condition appears in the description of the invariant part of the complement of the preceding class in $L(T)$.

We also mention the following result of Gulisashvili [8]: each function $f \in L(T)$ can be brought into the class $\bigcap_{p>2} A_p(T)$ by a "rearrangement" that is the identity outside a set of small measure.

The question of the relation between the topological and differentiability properties of a function relates to the same circle of questions. Bruckner and Hoffman first considered the question of conditions ensuring that a function can be brought into the class $C^1(T)$ by means of a homeomorphism of the circle. It turned out [4] that the following two conditions are necessary and sufficient for this:

$1°$. f has bounded variation; and

$2°$. the f-image of the set E_f of critical points has measure zero. (By definition, $t_0 \in E_f$ if f is not constant nor strictly monotone in any of the neighborhoods of t_0.)

A generalization to other classes of smoothness was obtained by Lebedev [18]. We present his result, which was first published in [24].

THEOREM 14. *A function in $C(T)$ can be brought into the class $C^k(T)$ (k a fixed positive integer) by means of a homeomorphism if and only if the above condition $2°$ holds and $\sum_\nu |\omega_\nu|^{1/k} < \infty$, where ω_ν is the oscillation of f on the open intervals forming the complement of E_f. The function f can be brought into C^∞ if this holds for all k.*

An analogous result was obtained independently by Laczkovich and Preiss [17].

It would be interesting to find multidimensional analogues of these results. It is possible that this problem is connected with methods of Kronrod and Vitushkin; see [7].

7. On orthogonal expansions

1. One result of the development of the theory of orthogonal series during the past 25 years is a clearer realization of the boundary that separates the general regularities inherent to all complete or all bounded orthonormal systems (ONS's) of functions from other properties where unexpected counterexamples are sometimes possible. For example, it was established that *an ONS Ψ_n cannot be uniformly bounded simultaneously with its Lebesgue functions $\mathscr{L}_n$* (Olevskiĭ, 1965). More precisely, if

$$|\varphi_n(x)| \leq K, \tag{8}$$

then on some set of positive measure

$$\overline{\lim_{n \to \infty}} \mathscr{L}_n(x) = \infty. \tag{9}$$

This means the impossibility of a bounded ONS providing each continuous function with an everywhere convergent Fourier expansion, or providing each function of class L with an expansion convergent in the mean. A little later (1966) we gave a sharp estimate of the rate of growth of the Lebesgue functions of a uniformly bounded ONS: for infinitely many n

$$\mathscr{L}_n(x) > \alpha \ln n \qquad (\forall x \in E, \text{ meas } E > 0). \tag{10}$$

It gives a lower estimate of the rate of divergence of Fourier series with respect to systems with (8). However, in contrast to the trigonometric case, relation (10) does not have as a consequence the corresponding smoothness of a function with divergent Fourier series: it is possible to construct a complete uniformly bounded ONS providing each function in a predetermined class H^ω with a uniformly convergent expansion. See [21], Chapter 1, for details on these results.

Other authors later developed this theme (Bochkarëv, Szarek, Bourgain, and others). In particular, the first of them showed (1975) that inequality (9) together with the Kolmogorov method for constructing divergent Fourier series enables one to construct, in systems with (8), class-L series that diverge on sets of positive measure.

For complete ONS's an approach was developed that is based on certain special properties of the classical Haar system χ_n. It first met approval in the proof of the impossibility of a complete ONS of unconditional convergence (Olevskiĭ and Ul′yanov, 1961). The extremal role of the Haar system among all complete systems was later discovered. Roughly speaking, we showed (1966) that if a Fourier series divergence phenomenon holds in some function class invariant under measure-preserving transformations of a closed interval, then such a phenomenon is unavoidable for an arbitrary complete ONS; see [21], Chapter 3. This result has a number of applications (one of them is Theorem 4, above). The approach based on the Haar system was later (1973) used by Arutyunyan in the problem of representing measurable functions by almost everywhere convergent series; he distinguished a broad class of ONS's, including the classical systems and their rearrangements, for which this problem has a positive solution. At the same time, there exists an example of a complete ONS for which only the functions of class L^2 have such a representation (Kashin, 1977). We remark further that the property "if the Fourier series of a function f in a complete ONS converges almost everywhere, then the sum is equal to f" can fail to hold in spaces barely extending L^2 ([21], Chapter 4).

2. Some of the results presented in this report can also be of interest from the point of view of the possibility of extending them to more or less general classes of ONS's. Let

$$A_p^\Psi = \{f; (f, \Psi_n) \in l_p\}.$$

The discrete problem of correction (§2), which does not impose restrictions on the relative dispositions of the bases, suggests that analogues of Theorems 2 and 3 are valid in a more general situation. In particular, it is not hard to extend these theorems to the Walsh system and systems close to it. Corresponding analogues for the Haar system were obtained even earlier by Fridlyand on the basis of a simpler approach [29]. On the other hand, Talalyan (1964) gave an example of a complete ONS Ψ with respect to which each function is correctable into the class A_1^Ψ. Such an example can be constructed from uniformly bounded trigonometric polynomials [29]. It would be interesting to distinguish a sufficiently general class of ONS's for which "noncorrectability" theorems hold. It should be noted that continuous functions with Carleman singularities exist with respect to arbitrary complete ONS's (Olevskiĭ, 1961). Also, for such systems the classes $H^{\alpha(p)}$ are not imbedded in A_p^Ψ (Mityagin and Bochkarëv, 1964).

We remark that the corresponding analogue of the Luzin homeomorphism problem has a positive solution for a system of characters on the group of p-adic integers (Gatesoupe [32]).

Concerning Theorem 12, we remark that the possibility of extending it to arbitrary complete ONS's has not been excluded.

The question of homeomorphisms acting in the classes A_p has apparently not been investigated for systems different from the trigonometric system (in particular, for the Haar system). Ul'yanov, in completing a broad investigation of the properties of the Haar system begun in the 1960s, studied the question of outer compositions acting in the classes A_1. He proved [28] that a function $\Phi : \mathbf{R} \to \mathbf{R}$ has the property that $f \in A_1^\chi \Rightarrow \Phi \circ f \in A_1^\chi$ if and only if it is a Lipschitz function. This condition is essentially weaker (locally) than the analyticity condition in the corresponding theorem of Lévy and Katznelson, which relates to $A(T)$. Ul'yanov assumed that a further weakening of the condition on Φ is impossible in the class of complete ONS's; this is consistent with the extremal role mentioned above for the Haar system.

BIBLIOGRAPHY

1. L. Alpár, *Convergence uniforme et changement de variable*, Studia Sci. Math. Hungar. **9** (1974), 267–275.

2. N. K. Bari, *Trigonometric series*, Fizmatgiz, Moscow, 1961; English transl., Vols. I, II, Macmillan, New York, and Pergamon Press, Oxford, 1964.

3. Albert Baernstein II and Daniel Waterman, *Functions whose Fourier series converge uniformly for every change of variable*, Indiana Univ. Math. J. **22** (1972/73), 569–576.

4. Andrew M. Bruckner, *Differentiation of real functions*, Lecture Notes in Math., vol. 659, Springer-Verlag, 1978.

5. S. A. Vinogradov, *Convergence almost everywhere of Fourier series of functions in L^2, and the behavior of the coefficients of uniformly convergent Fourier series*, Dokl. Akad. Nauk SSSR **230** (1976), 508–511; English transl. in Soviet Math. Dokl. **17** (1976).

6. S. A. Vinogradov and S. V. Hruščëv [Khrushchëv], *Free interpolation in the space of uniformly convergent Taylor series*, Complex Analysis and Spectral Theory (Leningrad, 1979/80), Lecture Notes in Math., vol. 864, Springer-Verlag, 1981, pp. 171–213.

7. A. G. Vitushkin, *On multidimensional variations*, GITTL, Moscow, 1955. (Russian)

8. A. B. Gulisashvili, *On singularities of integrable functions*, Zap. Nauchn. Sem. Leningrad. Otdel. Mat. Inst. Steklov. (LOMI) **113** (1981), 76–96; English transl. in J. Soviet Math. **22** (1983), no. 6.

9. B. N. Demenko, *On p-Helson curves on the plane*, Mat. Zametki **39** (1986), 349–359; English transl. in Math Notes **39** (1986).

10. Jean-Pierre Kahane, *Séries de Fourier absolument convergentes*, Springer-Verlag, 1970.

11. ____, *Quatre leçons sur les homéomorphismes du cercle et les séries de Fourier*, Topics in Modern Harmonic Analysis (Proc. Sem., Turin and Milan, 1982; L. De-Michele and F. Ricci, editors), Vol. II, Ist. Naz. Alta Mat. F. Severi, Rome, 1983, pp. 955–990.

12. Jean-Pierre Kahane and Yitzhak Katznelson, *Homéomorphismes du cercle et séries de Fourier absolument convergentes*, C. R. Acad. Sci. Paris Sér. I Math. **292** (1981), 271–273.

13. Y. Katznelson, *On a theorem of Menchoff*, Proc. Amer. Math. Soc. **53** (1975), 396–398.

14. B. S. Kashin, *On some properties of a space of trigonometric polynomials connected with uniform convergence*, Soobshch. Akad. Nauk Gruzin. SSR **93** (1979), 281–284. (Russian)

15. S. V. Kislyakov, *A quantitative aspect of correction theorems*, Zap. Nauchn. Sem. Leningrad. Otdel. Mat. Inst. Steklov. (LOMI) **92** (1979), 182–191. (Russian)

16. Paul J. Cohen, *On a conjecture of Littlewood and idempotent measures*, Amer. J. Math. **82** (1960), 191–212.

17. M. Laczkovich and D. Preiss, *α-variation and transformation into C^n functions*, Indiana Univ. Math. J. **34** (1985), 405–424.

18. V. V. Lebedev, *Homeomorphisms of a closed interval and smoothness of a function*, Mat. Zametki **40** (1986), 364–373; English transl. in Math. Notes **40** (1986).

19. O. Carruth McGehee and Gordon S. Woodward, *Continuous manifolds in $\mathbf{R}^n$ that are sets of interpolation for the Fourier algebra*, Ark. Mat. **20** (1982) 169–199.

20. Daniel M. Oberlin, *A Rudin-Carleson theorem for uniformly convergent Taylor series*, Michigan J. Math. **27** (1980), 309–313.

21. A. M. Olevskiĭ, *Fourier series with respect to general orthogonal systems*, Springer-Verlag, 1975.

22. ____, *The existence of functions with nonremovable Carleman singularities*, Dokl. Akad. Nauk SSSR **238** (1978), 796–799; English transl. in Soviet Math. Dokl. **19** (1978).

23. ____, *Change of variable and absolute convergence of Fourier series*, Dokl. Akad. Nauk SSSR **256** (1981), 284–287; English transl. in Soviet Math. Dokl. **23** (1981).

24. ____, *Modifications of functions and Fourier series*, Uspekhi Mat. Nauk **40** (1985), no. 3 (243), 157–193; English transl. in Russian Math. Surveys **40** (1985).

25. ____, *On the algebra of functions generated by uniformly convergent Fourier series*, Dokl. Akad. Nauk SSSR **297** (1987), 798–800; English transl. in Soviet Math. Dokl. **36** (1988).

26. A. A. Saakyan, *Integral moduli of smoothness and the Fourier coefficients of the composition of functions*, Mat. Sb. **110** (**152**) (1979), 597–608; English transl. in Math. USSR Sb. **38** (1981).

27. P. L. Ul'yanov, *Solved and unsolved problems in the theory of trigonometric and orthogonal series*, Uspekhi Mat. Nauk **19** (1964), no. 1 (115), 3–69; English transl. in Russian Math. Surveys **19** (1964).

28. ____, *Absolute convergence of Fourier-Haar series for superpositions of functions*, Anal. Math. **4** (1978), 225–236. (Russian)

29. Yu. S. Fridlyand, *On a nonremovable Carleman singularity for the Haar system*, Mat. Zametki **14** (1973), 799–807; English transl. in Math Notes **14** (1973).

30. S. V. Khrushchev, *Men'shov's correction theorem and Gaussian processes*, Trudy Mat. Inst. Steklov. **15** (1981), 151–183; English transl. in Proc. Steklov Inst. Math. **1983**, no. 1 (155).

31. O. D. Tsereteli, *On conjugate functions*, Mat. Zametki **22** (1977), 771–783; English transl. in Math. Notes **22** (1977).

32. M. Gatesoupe, *Topics in harmonic analysis on abelian compact groups homeomorphic with the Cantor set*, Topics in Modern Harmonic Analysis (Proc. Sem., Turin and Milan, 1982; L. De-Michele and F. Ricci, editors), Vol. II, Ist. Naz. Alta Mat. F. Severi, Rome, 1983, pp. 991–1009.

Moscow Institute of Electronic Machine Construction
Moscow 109028
USSR

Translated by H. H. McFADEN

Amer. Math. Soc. Transl.
(2) Vol. **147**, 1990

The Problem of Guaranteed Precision
in Numerical Methods of Linear Algebra

S. K. GODUNOV

We shall discuss problems where matrices and vectors corresponding to given conditions are known with some relative error (measured in a Euclidean metric). Instead of A_0 and f_0 only their approximations A and f, with

$$\|A - A_0\| < \varepsilon \|A_0\|, \qquad \|f - f_0\| < \varepsilon \|f_0\|,$$

are accessible, where ε is a degree of accuracy (relative error). Typical values are 10^{-5}, 10^{-10}, 10^{-30}, ...

The above assumption restricts the class of problems for which it is possible to work out efficient methods with guaranteed precision. If errors in conditions of order ε lead to errors in results of order 1, then there is no hope of constructing an efficient algorithm. Problems of this kind are called *pathological*. Sometimes we can avoid this pathology by changing the way a problem is formulated.

Calculation of the spectrum of A is frequently used when analyzing the stability of a solution of a system $\dot{x} = Ax$. A typical pathological example arises when we consider a two-diagonal $\mathcal{N} \times \mathcal{N}$ matrix A_0 where on the main diagonal we have -1 everywhere and on the upper subdiagonal we have 10 everywhere. All eigenvalues $\lambda(A_0)$ are equal to -1, and stability holds. For $\mathcal{N} = 25$ we construct the matrix A_ω by replacing the zero in the left lower corner of A_0 by $\omega = -10 \times 2^{-75} \approx -2.6 \times 10^{-22}$. Now A_0 has an eigenvalue $\lambda(A_\omega) = +\frac{1}{4}$. On a computer with $\varepsilon = 10^{-20}$ the matrices A_0 and A_ω are indistinguishable. Of course, the matrix A_0 can be transformed by the similarity transformation $W^{-1}A_0 W = \tilde{A}_0$, where $W = \operatorname{diag}(1, 10^{-2}, 10^{-4}, \ldots, 10^{-48})$, and then we can calculate eigenvalues

1980 *Mathematics Subject Classification* (1985 *Revision*). Primary 65F15.
Translation of Proc. Internat. Congr. Math. (Berkeley, Calif., 1986), Vol. 2, Amer. Math. Soc., Providence, R.I., 1987, pp. 1353–1361; MR **89g**:65059.

$\lambda(\tilde{A}_0)$ which are identical with $\lambda(A_0)$. This frequently used transformation leads to $\tilde{A}_0$ with exceptionally well-conditioned eigenvalues, but justification of the above transformation is questionable since W is practically singular and $W^{-1}A_\omega W$ differs from $W^{-1}A_0 W$ by the nonnegligible element $10^{24}\omega = -260$ in the left lower corner.

We propose another approach for the analysis of stability of $\dot{x} = Ax$. Instead of $\lambda_i(A)$ we recommend [1] defining *quality of stability* by

$$\kappa(A) = \sup_{x(0)} \frac{\int_0^\infty \|x(t)\|^2 dt}{\int_0^\infty \exp(-2t\|A\|)\cdot\|x(0)\|^2 dt}$$

(if $\dot{x} = Ax$ is not asymptotically stable as $t \to \infty$, then $\kappa(A) = \infty$). For the matrix A_0 we have $\kappa(A_0) > 10^{23}$, i.e., $\dot{x} = A_0 x$ is practically unstable despite the fact that $\lambda_i(A_0) = -1$. In fact, if $x_1(0) = x_2(0) = \cdots = x_{24}(0) = 0$ and $x_{25}(0) = \xi = \sqrt{48\pi} \times 10^{-23} \approx 1.23 \times 10^{-22}$, then for $t = 24$ the solution $x_j(t) = \xi(10^{25-j}/j!)t^{25-j}e^{-t}$ has the component $x_1(24) = (10\cdot 24/e)^{24}\cdot(\sqrt{48\pi}\cdot 10^{-23}/24!) \approx 10$.

There is an interesting algebraic definition $\kappa(A) = \|H\|$ (see [2]), where H is the positive definite solution of the equation $HA + A^*H = -2\|A\|\cdot I$. (If the equation has no solution or H is not positive definite, then $\kappa(A) = \infty$.) It can be shown that for $t > 0$

$$\|e^{tA}\| \le \sqrt{\kappa(A)}\exp\left[-t\frac{\|A\|}{\kappa(A)}\right] \tag{1}$$

and for $\|B\|/\|A\| < 1/[10\kappa(A)^2]$

$$|\kappa(A+B) - \kappa(B)| < 13\kappa(A)^3\frac{\|B\|}{\|A\|}. \tag{2}$$

The operator H can be conveniently evaluated using the Lyapunov formula $H = 2\|A\|\int_0^\infty e^{tA^*}e^{tA}dt$. We note that if Π is an orthogonal projection (i.e., $\Pi^* = \Pi$, $\Pi^2 = \Pi$, and consequently $\Pi A\Pi = A\Pi$) on an invariant (under A) subspace such that all eigenvalues of A are negative, then we can define the matrix integrals

$$y_k = \int_0^{2^k\tau} \Pi e^{t\Pi A^*}Ce^{tA\Pi}\Pi dt, \tag{3}$$

where $C = C^*$. For Hurwitzian A, $\Pi = I$, $C = 2\|A\|\cdot I$ and $\tau = 1/(2\|A\|)$ the limit $y = \lim_{k\to\infty} y_k$ coincides with H. The well-known procedure of Davison and Man [6] for the evaluation of y_k-like integrals starts with the definition of y_1 by Taylor's formula and $B_1 = e^{\tau A\Pi}\Pi$. Then the recurrent formulas

$$B_k = B_{k-1}^2, \qquad y_k = y_{k-1} + B_{k-1}^* y_{k-1} B_{k-1} \tag{4}$$

are used.

Let us study stability ($\Pi = I$, $C = 2\|A\| \cdot I$) using (1), and let us choose κ^* such that for $\kappa(A) > \kappa^*$ the system $\dot{x} = Ax$ is practically unstable. Then we can estimate how many steps (iterations) in (4), $\tau = 1/(2\|A\|)$, are necessary for the following inequality to hold:

$$(5) \qquad \left\| A^* y_j + y_j A + 2\|A\| \cdot I \right\| \leq 2\rho\|A\|, \quad \text{where } 0 < \rho < 1,$$

provided $\kappa(A) < \kappa^*$. Obviously, it is true for $j > 1 + \log_2[\kappa^* \ln(2\kappa^*/\rho)]$. Moreover, for such j we have, for any X_j such that $\|X_j - y_j\| \leq \rho/2$, the following inequality:

$$\left\| A^* X_j + X_j A + 2\|A\| \cdot I \right\| \leq 2\rho\|A\|.$$

For X_j we can use an approximate value from calculations. If (6) holds then (see [3])

$$(7) \qquad \frac{\|H - X_j\|}{\|X_j\|} < \frac{\rho}{1 - \rho},$$

$$\frac{1 - 2\rho}{1 - \rho} \|X_j\| < \kappa(A) < \frac{1}{1 - \rho} \|X_j\|.$$

Assuming $\kappa(A) < \kappa^*$, error estimates [4] based on (1) for a calculation of a matrix exponent were used in [3]. We execute j steps (iterations) in (4). If (6) does not hold, then either $\kappa(A) > \kappa^*$ or we evaluate an approximate value $\kappa(A)$. We can find $\kappa(A)$ iteratively with an accuracy limited only by computer precision. Simultaneously for $\kappa(A) < \kappa^*$ we calculate the Lyapunov function (Hx, x). We shall list $\kappa(A_0)$ for the above A_0's, $3 \leq \mathcal{N} \leq 8$:

$$\mathcal{N} = 3, \quad \kappa = 4.05 \cdot 10^4; \qquad \mathcal{N} = 6, \quad \kappa = 2.7 \cdot 10^{10};$$
$$\mathcal{N} = 4, \quad \kappa = 3.40 \cdot 10^6; \qquad \mathcal{N} = 7, \quad \kappa = 2.5 \cdot 10^{12};$$
$$\mathcal{N} = 5, \quad \kappa = 3.00 \cdot 10^8; \qquad \mathcal{N} = 8, \quad \kappa = 2.3 \cdot 10^{14}.$$

We also note that the condition number μ of the system of linear equations associated with $HA + A^*H = -C$ is majorized by $\kappa(A)$ as follows:

$$\mu < \mathcal{N}\kappa(A)^2.$$

The following problem of dichotomy of a matrix spectrum is a generalization of the Hurwitz problem. Given a number p, we need to find the number of roots of $\det(A - \lambda I)$ such that $\text{Re}\,\lambda < p$ and such that $\text{Re}\,\lambda > p$. Particularly, if $p = 0$ we need to know how many roots are in the left half-plane and how many are in the right half-plane, and if there are any imaginary roots $\lambda = i\omega$. The dichotomy problem arises, for example, when we construct a Green matrix $G(t)$, bounded for $-\infty < t < \infty$, which satisfies the equation

$$(8) \qquad \frac{d}{dt}G(t) = AG(t) + \delta(t) \cdot I.$$

This equation has a solution only if the $\lambda_j(A)$ are not on the imaginary axis. In addition,

(9)
$$\Pi_+ = G(-0)\left[G^*(+0)G(+0) + G^*(-0)G(-0)\right]^{-1}G^*(-0),$$

$$\Pi_- = G(+0)\left[G^*(+0)G(+0) + G^*(-0)G(-0)\right]^{-1}G^*(+0)$$

are orthogonal projections on (invariant under A) subspaces with $\lambda_j(A) > 0$ and $\lambda_j(A) < 0$ respectively. Dimensions of the subspaces are given by $\mathcal{N}_\pm = \operatorname{tr}\Pi_\pm$. We also mention the identities

(10)
$$e^{tA}G(-0) = e^{tA\Pi_+}G(-0) = e^{tA\Pi_+}\Pi_+ G(-0) \qquad (t < 0),$$

$$e^{tA}G(+0) = e^{tA\Pi_-}G(+0) = e^{tA\Pi_-}\Pi_- G(+0) \qquad (t > 0).$$

In [5] we presented as a criterion of dichotomy the quantity $\kappa(A) = 2\|A\|\cdot\|H\|$ $(H = H_+ + H_-)$, where

(11)
$$H_+ = \int_0^\infty G^*(t)G(t)\,dt = G^*(+0)y^{(+)}G(+0),$$

$$H_- = \int_{-\infty}^0 G^*(t)G(t)\,dt = G^*(-0)y^{(-)}G(-0),$$

and

(12)
$$y^{(+)} = \int_0^\infty \Pi_- e^{t\Pi_- A^*}e^{tA\Pi_-}\Pi_-\,dt,$$

$$y^{(-)} = \int_0^\infty \Pi_+ e^{-t\Pi_+ A^*}e^{-tA\Pi_+}\Pi_+\,dt.$$

If we have already precomputed $G(\pm 0)$ and $\Pi_\pm$, then we can use (5) to calculate the integrals (11) and (12).

It has been shown that $\|G(t)\| \le \kappa(A)\exp[-|t|\cdot\|A\|/\kappa(A)]$. It is convenient to consider, instead of $G(t)$, Green's matrices $G_n(t)$ of boundary problems on a finite interval $|t| < n/(2\|A\|)$ such that $G_n'(t) = AG_n(t) + \delta(t)\cdot I$ and $G_n[n/(2\|A\|)] = G_n[-n/(2\|A\|)]$. In addition,

(13)
$$G_n(t) = \sum_{k=-\infty}^\infty G(t + kn/\|A\|),$$

$$\|G_n(t) - G(t)\| \le 2\kappa(A)\exp\left[-\frac{n}{2\kappa(A)}\right]\cdot\left\{1 - \exp\left[-\frac{n}{\kappa(A)}\right]\right\}^{-1},$$

and if $\kappa(A) < \infty$ then the matrices

(14) $$\Pi_\pm^{(n)} = G_n(\mp 0)\left[G_n^*(+0)G_n(+0) + G^*(-0)G_n(-0)\right]^{-1}G_n^*(\mp 0)$$

converge to projections $\Pi_\pm$ as $n \to \infty$.

Putting $\mathscr{P}_0 = \mathscr{Q}_0 = (1/\sqrt{2})I$, we define $\mathscr{P}_{i+1}$, $\mathscr{Q}_{i+1}$, and upper triangular $\mathscr{R}_{i+1}$ recursively from the following identities:

(15)
$$\begin{bmatrix} e^{\tau A} & \mathscr{Q}_i \\ e^{-\tau A} & \mathscr{P}_i \end{bmatrix} = \begin{bmatrix} \mathscr{Q}_{i+1} \\ \mathscr{P}_{i+1} \end{bmatrix} \mathscr{R}_{i+1}, \qquad \mathscr{Q}_{i+1}^* \mathscr{Q}_{i+1} + \mathscr{P}_{i+1}^* \mathscr{P}_{i+1} = I,$$

where $\tau = 1/(2\|A\|)$. In fact, this recursion is the well-known orthogonal power method for block-diagonal matrices of doubled order with diagonal blocks $e^{\pm\tau A}$. Any solution of the matrix equation $Z' = AZ$ on the interval $[-n\tau, n\tau]$ with the point $t = 0$ deleted (i.e., on $[-n\tau, 0)\cup(0, n\tau]$) satisfying the condition $Z(-n\tau) = Z(n\tau)$ can be represented by

$$Z(t) = \begin{cases} e^{tA}\mathscr{Q}_n T_n & (-n\tau \le t < 0), \\ e^{tA}\mathscr{P}_n T_n & (0 < t < n\tau), \end{cases}$$

with some T_n. In particular, $Z(-0) = \mathscr{Q}_n T_n$, and $Z(+0) = \mathscr{P}_n T_n$. If we put $T_n = (\mathscr{P}_n - \mathscr{Q}_n)^{-1}$, then $Z(+0) - Z(-0) = I$ and consequently $Z(t) = G_n(t)$. Thus

(16)
$$G_n(+0) = \mathscr{P}_n(\mathscr{P}_n - \mathscr{Q}_n)^{-1} = \mathscr{P}_n T_n,$$
$$G_n(-0) = \mathscr{Q}_n(\mathscr{P}_n - \mathscr{Q}_n)^{-1} = \mathscr{Q}_n T_n.$$

The estimates

$$\|T_n^{-1}\| \le 2 \quad \text{and} \quad \|T_n\| \le 2\kappa(A)\left\{1 + 2\frac{\exp\left[-\frac{n}{2\kappa(A)}\right]}{1 - \exp\left[-\frac{n}{\kappa(A)}\right]}\right\}$$

make it possible to calculate $G_n(+0)$ and $G_n(-0)$ provided that $\kappa(A)$ is not too large.

Note that the calculations (we just sketched the basic steps) can be organized as a process to investigate stability, which was described above. This either leads to the inequality $\kappa(A) > \kappa^*$, or determines $\kappa(A)$, H, and $\Pi_\pm$. The projections are calculated by the following formulas:

$$\Pi_+^{(n)} = \mathscr{Q}_n \mathscr{Q}_n^*, \qquad \Pi_-^{(n)} = \mathscr{P}_n \mathscr{P}_n^*.$$

As an example we shall present the calculation of $\kappa(A - pI)$ for an upper two-diagonal matrix A of order 21. On the main diagonal of A we have the eigenvalues $-28, -27, \ldots, -16, -15, +21, +20, \ldots, +16, +15$, and on the subdiagonal we have $14, \ldots, 14$ (13 times), then 0 and then $7, \ldots, 7$ (6 times). The projections Π_+ and Π_- are orthogonal ($\Pi_+\Pi_- = \Pi_-\Pi_+ = 0$, $\mathscr{N}_+ = 7$, and $\mathscr{N}_- = 14$).

It turned out that $\kappa(A) = 8.08$ and on the intervals $-31.7 < p < -10.5$ and $14.8 < p < 21.3$, which cover the negative and positive part of the spectrum, $\kappa(A - pI)$ is practically infinite ($\kappa(A - pI) > \kappa^* = 10^8$). For p

outside of the intervals we have the following values for $\kappa(A - pI)$:

p	-60	-40	-32	-9.5	-8.5	-6.5
κ	3.99	27.9	$2.05 \cdot 10^5$	$5.13 \cdot 10^3$	$9.91 \cdot 10^2$	99.99
p	-4.5	-0.5	4.5	8.5	10.5	11.5
κ	28.2	8.8	7.1	20.4	62.9	$1.7 \cdot 10^2$
p	12.5	13.5	14.5	21.5	22.5	23.5
κ	$88 \cdot 10^2$	$1.3 \cdot 10^4$	$1.88 \cdot 10^5$	$2.4 \cdot 10^7$	$1.78 \cdot 10^4$	$1.56 \cdot 10^2$

Thus the dichotomy of the spectrum of A on the parts with $\operatorname{Re}\lambda > 0$ and $\operatorname{Re}\lambda < 0$ can be carried out, but the parts of the spectrum with $\operatorname{Re}\lambda < 17.5$ and $\operatorname{Re}\lambda > 17.5$ are practically inseparable, although for $\lambda = 17.5$ there is no discrete spectrum.

The problem of how spectral problems must be formulated arises from the study of spectra of sequences of difference operators [7]–[10]. We also mention the recently constructed example (see [11]) of a matrix with a spectrum which can be approximated (with high accuracy) by all points of two flat domains of a bizarre form. These domains cannot be separated by a line or a circle. Thus it is not possible to construct corresponding projections by using a QR-algorithm or an orthogonal power method.

Our approach for avoiding pathological cases in a calculation of the spectrum of arbitrary matrices is based on recasting the problem into another that is more specific and is especially oriented toward well-defined applications.

In a number of cases in linear algebra pathology appears not because we solve ill-conditioned problems, but rather because the algorithm has in fact a hidden defect. Such a defect is difficult to detect and thus difficult to establish.

This point will be illustrated by an example of the exhaustion algorithm (i.e., diagonalization of a tri-diagonal matrix A by sequentially annihilating matrix elements on subdiagonals). First it is necessary to consider a calculation of an eigenvector of A when we have approximately precalculated $\lambda(A)$ (e.g., by a bisection method). The last problem consists of a solution of homogeneous equations

$$(d_1 - \lambda)u_1 - b_2 u_2 = 0,$$
$$-b_j u_{j-1} + (d_j - \lambda)u_j - b_{j+1} u_{j+1} = 0, \qquad 2 \le j \le m - 1,$$
$$-b_m u_{m-1} + (d_m - \lambda)u_m = 0.$$

We always have $b_i > 0$. We can put $u_1 = 1$; then $u_2 = (d_2 - \lambda)/b_2$ and all remaining u_k's ($3 \le k \le m$) are given by the recurrent relation $u_k = [-b_{k-1}u_{k-2} + (d_k - \lambda)u_{k-1}]/b_k$. The last row $(-b_m, d_m)$ of A does not participate in this calculation. Thus we can check the calculation by verifying that the last element v_m of the residual vector $v = (A - \lambda I)u$ is equal to zero.

It turns out that infinitesimal errors in an eigenvalue can cause catastrophic inconsistencies in the above homogeneous equations. Let us consider a symmetric tri-diagonal Jacobian matrix of the fifth order with main diagonal $2, 1 + \delta, 2\delta, 1 + \delta, 2$ and subdiagonal $-1, -\delta, -\delta, -1$. This matrix has an isolated eigenvalue in the interval $(0, 3\delta)$. If δ is very small, we can assume that $\lambda \approx 0$. Putting $u_1 = 1$ and calculating, as described above, the remaining vector elements $u = (1, 2, 2 + 1/\delta, 2 + 2/\delta, 3 + 2/\delta)^T$, we obtain for the residue vector $v = (0, 0, 0, 0, 4 + 2/\delta)^T$. In addition, if $\delta \to 0$, then $\|v\|/\|u\| = (4\delta + 2)/\sqrt{22\delta^2 + 24\delta + 9} \to \frac{2}{3}$. We can avoid this paradox if we calculate (with some precaution) the ratios $\mathscr{P}_i = u_{i-1}/u_i$ (Sturm sequence) from left to right by $g_i = d_i - \lambda$, $\mathscr{P}'_1 = b_1 = 0$, and $\mathscr{P}'_i = b_i/(g_{i-1} - b_{i-1}\mathscr{P}'_{i-1})$, and then once again, now from right to left, by $b_{m+1} = 0$, $\mathscr{P}''_{m+1} = \infty$, and $\mathscr{P}''_i = (g_i - b_{i+1}/\mathscr{P}''_{i+1})/b_i$. Now choosing, according to the rule we shall state below, $i = i_0$, we put $\mathscr{P}_i = \mathscr{P}'_i$ if $i < i_0$ and $\mathscr{P}_i = \mathscr{P}''_i$ if $i > i_0$. Before we describe precautionary measures we must follow during the calculation of the Sturm sequence (and the choice of i_0), we have to introduce special continuous monotone functions $\omega = \omega(a, g, b, \gamma)$ and its inverse $\gamma = \gamma(a, g, b, \omega)$, which are defined for $-\infty < \gamma < \infty$ and $-\infty < \omega < \infty$. Using these functions $(a, b > 0)$, we realize the uniformization of the relation $\tan \omega = b/(g - a \tan \gamma)$. If we put $\mathscr{P}'_i = \tan \varphi_i$ and $\mathscr{P}''_i = \tan \psi_i$, then φ_i and ψ_i satisfy the following identities: $\varphi_1 = 0$, $\varphi_i = \omega(b_i, d_i - \lambda, b_{i-1}, \varphi_{i-1})$ $(i > 1)$, $\psi_m = (n - \frac{1}{2})\pi$, and $\psi_i = \gamma(b_{i+1}, d_{i+1} - \lambda, b_i, \psi_{i+1})$ $(i < m)$.

If λ is an eigenvalue $\lambda = \lambda_n$, then $\varphi_i = \psi_i$. The Sturm theorem formulated in terms of φ_i and ψ_i states that for increasing λ, any φ_i increases and any ψ_i decreases. This theorem can be generalized so that it shows if φ_i or ψ_i is increasing or decreasing when any parameter b_j, d_k, or a_i is increasing or decreasing. Using this generalization, it is not difficult to organize the calculation of $\mathscr{P}'_i$ and $\mathscr{P}''_i$ (rounding upward or downward) in such a way that φ'_i and ψ''_i corresponding to the calculated Sturm sequence will majorize $\varphi_i = \psi_i$ corresponding to exact $\mathscr{P}_i$ with exact λ. In addition, it is easy to verify that we can find at least one number i_0 such that $\psi''_{i_0-1} > \varphi'_{i_0-1}$ and $\psi''_{i_0} < \varphi'_{i_0}$. The number i_0 forms a boundary. Starting from this boundary, we must replace any $\mathscr{P}'_i$ (from the Sturm sequence) by $\mathscr{P}''_i$. For real calculations it is not necessary to evaluate φ'_i and ψ''_i, since rules for the choice of i_0 can be expressed in terms of $\mathscr{P}'_i$ and $\mathscr{P}''_i$ only. Of course, the rules are then less obvious. This idea is described in detail in [12], and [13], where it is shown that in the error estimate $\|Au - \lambda u\| < \varepsilon \|u\|$ the relative error ε depends only on computer precision and is independent of the order m of the Jacobian matrix A. Even if an eigenvalue almost fails to be simple, the relative error ε is the same as for isolated λ. The relative error is proportional (with a small coefficient) to the difference between one and the next closest number that can be represented on a computer.

Using $\mathscr{P}_i = u_{i-1}/u_i$ calculated by the above version of the Sturm method, we define the parameters of a two-dimensional rotation as follows:

$$c_1 = 1, \qquad c_i = (c_{i-1}\operatorname{sgn}\mathscr{P}_i)/\sqrt{c_{i-1}^2 + \mathscr{P}_i^2}, \qquad s_i = |\mathscr{P}_i|/\sqrt{c_i^2 + \mathscr{P}_i^2}$$

(one step of exhaustion). A tri-diagonal structure of a Jacobian operator A is invariant under the orthogonal transformation. New elements $\overline{d}_i$ on the main diagonal and $\overline{b}_i$ on the subdiagonal are given by

$$\overline{d}_i = d_{i+1} - (c_{i+1}c_i b_{i+1}/s_{i+1}) + (c_{i+2}c_{i+1}b_{i+2}/s_{i+2}) \qquad (1 \le i \le m-1),$$
$$\overline{d}_m = \lambda_n, \qquad \overline{b}_m = 0, \qquad \overline{b}_i = s_i b_{i+1}/s_{i+1} \qquad (2 \le i \le m-1).$$

Using the above formulas, we can develop an algorithm with a guaranteed precision of calculation for a transformed matrix

$$\|\overline{A}_{\text{calc}} - \overline{A}\| \approx m^{3/2}\varepsilon\|A\|.$$

In addition, there is no room for paradoxes such as pathological cases where $\overline{b}_m$ is different from zero when we diagonalize a Jacobian matrix by a two-dimensional rotation with ordinary sequentially defined parameters [14]. Numerical experiments revealed that these paradoxes appear exactly in such cases where sequentially defined elements of an eigenvector do not make it possible to satisfy the last equation, $-b_m u_{m-1} + (d_m - \lambda)u_m = 0$.

Similarly to the way in which the described method leads to a reliable version of exhaustion of tri-diagonal matrices [15], [16], [18], it can also be used for singular exhaustion of two-diagonal matrices. In this case the method consists of a preliminary definition of ratios of elements of singular vectors and the use of these ratios for a calculation of parameters of two-dimensional rotations. As a result we obtain a new version of the SVD-algorithm which is similar to the algorithm of Golub and Kahan [19] but which can be rigorously justified. We note that as a rule when implementing the SVD-algorithm we use iterative corrections. In most cases this avoids pathology. The algorithm from [15] and [18] has an overhead due to the calculation (as accurate as possible) of a singular number. On the other hand, the elimination process then runs without iterative corrections.

BIBLIOGRAPHY

1. S. K. Godounov [Godunov] and A. J. Boulgakov [A. Ya. Bulgakov], *Difficultés calculatives dans le problème de Hurwitz et méthodes à les surmonter (aspect calculatif du problème de Hurwitz)*, Analysis and Optimisation of Systems (Proc. Fifth Internat. Conf., Versailles, 1982), Lecture Notes in Control and Information Sci., vol. 44, Springer-Verlag, 1982, pp. 846–851; English abstract, ibid., p. 845.

2. A. Ya. Bulgakov, *An effectively calculable parameter for the stability property of a system of linear differential equations with constant coefficients*, Sibirsk. Mat. Zh. **21** (1980), no. 3, 32–41; English transl. in Siberian Math. J. **21** (1980).

3. A. Ya. Bulgakov and S. K. Godunov, *A calculation of positive definite solutions of the Lyapunov equation*, Numerical Methods of Linear Algebra, Trudy Inst. Mat. (Novosibirsk) **6** (1985), 17–38. (Russian)

4. A. Ya. Bulgakov, *A calculation of* exp *of an asymptotically stable matrix*, Numerical Methods of Linear Algebra, Trudy Inst. Mat. (Novosibirsk) **6** (1985), 4–17. (Russian)

5. A. Ya. Bulgakov and S. K. Godunov, *Parameter of matrix spectrum dichotomy and a scheme of its calculation*, Preprint No. 28, Inst. Mat. Sibirsk. Otdel. Akad. Nauk SSSR, Novosibirsk, 1985. (Russian) RZh Mat. **1986**, 561235.

6. E. J. Davison and F. T. Man, *The numerical solution of $A'Q + QA = -C$*, IEEE Trans. Automatic Control **AC-13** (1968), 448–449.

7. S. K. Godunov and V. S. Ryaben'kii, *Introduction to the theory of difference schemes*, Fizmatgiz, Moscow, 1962. (Russian; English transl., [9])

8. ____, *Spectral stability criteria for boundary value problems for nonselfadjoint difference equations*, Uspekhi Mat. Nauk **18** (1963) no. 3 (111), 3–14; English transl. in Russian Math. Surveys **18** (1963).

9. ____, *Theory of difference schemes: an introduction*, North-Holland, Amsterdam, and Interscience, New York, 1964.

10. Robert D. Richtmyer and K. W. Morton, *Difference methods for initial-value problems*, 2nd ed., Interscience, 1967.

11. V. I. Kostin and Sh. I. Razzakov, *On convergence of the orthogonal power method for calculating a spectrum*, Numerical Methods of Linear Algebra, Trudy Inst. Mat. (Novosibirsk) **6** (1985), 55–84. (Russian)

12. S. K. Godunov, V. I. Kostin, and A. D. Mitchenko, *Eigenvector calculations for a symmetric tridiagonal matrix*, Preprint No. 44, Inst. Mat. Sibirsk. Otdel. Akad. Nauk SSSR, Novosibirsk, 1983. (Russian) R. Zh. Mat. **1984**, 361156.

13. ____, *Calculating the eigenvector of a symmetric tri-diagonal matrix*, Sibirsk. Mat. Zh. **26** (1985), no. 5, 71–85; English transl. in Siberian Math. J. **26** (1985).

14. H. Rutishauser, *On Jacobi rotation patterns*, Experimental Arithmetic, High Speed Computing and Mathematics, Proc. Sympos. Appl. Math., vol. 15, Amer. Math. Soc., Providence, R. I., 1963, pp. 219–239.

15. A. D. Mitchenko, *Elimination algorithms for symmetric tridiagonal and two-diagonal matrices*, Preprint No. 59, Inst. Mat. Sibirsk. Otdel. Akad. Nauk SSSR, Novosibirsk, 1984. (Russian) R. Zh. Mat. **1985**, 161302.

16. ____, *Consideration of numerical errors in an elimination algorithm for symmetric tri-diagonal matrices*, Preprint No. 60, Inst. Mat. Sibirsk. Otdel. Akad. Nauk SSSR, Novosibirsk, 1984. (Russian) R. Zh. Mat. **1985**, 161284.

17. ____, *Consideration of numerical errors in an elimination algorithm for symmetric two-diagonal matrices*, Preprint No. 61, Inst. Mat. Sibirsk. Otdel. Akad. Nauk SSSR, Novosibirsk, 1984. (Russian) R. Zh. Mat. **1984**, 1261308.

18. A. D. Mitchenko, *Elimination algorithms for symmetric tridiagonal and two-diagonal matrices with a guaranteed precision*, Numerical Methods of Linear Algebra, Trudy Inst. Mat. (Novosibirsk) **6** (1985), 110–161. (Russian)

19. G. Golub and W. Kahan, *Calculating the singular values and pseudo-inverse of a matrix*, J. Soc. Indust. Appl. Math. Ser. B Numer. Anal. **2** (1965), 205–224.

Institute of Mathematics
  Siberian Branch
  Academy of Sciences of the USSR
  Novosibirsk

Translated by ALEX HOLUBEC

Amer. Math. Soc. Transl.
(2) Vol. **147**, 1990

Lower Bounds for Monotone Complexity
of Boolean Functions

A. A. RAZBOROV

The main purpose of this report is to elucidate the new results in superpoly-nomial lower bounds for monotone complexity of natural Boolean functions that have been obtained in the last two years. We will also briefly mention some old results in this direction. In conclusion we will touch upon another restriction on functional circuits, a restriction on the depth, since definite progress has been achieved for problems in this area in the last few years.

We start with the main definitions. By a *functional circuit with n inputs* we mean a sequence of Boolean functions in n variables

$$\{f_i(x_1, \ldots, x_n)\}_{i=1}^t, \tag{1}$$

in which, for any $1 \le i \le t$, one of the three following possibilities is realized:

    a) $\exists j \ (1 \le j \le n) \ f_i = x_j$,

    b) $\exists i_1, i_2 < i \ \exists * \in \{\&, \vee\} \ (f_i = f_{i_1} * f_{i_2})$,

    c) $\exists i_1 < i \ (f_i = \neg f_{i_1})$. $\tag{2}$

A circuit (1) *computes* a function f if $\exists i \ (1 \le i \le t) \ f_i = f$. The number t is called the *size* of the circuit. The *combinational complexity* $L(f)$ of a function f is the minimal possible size of a functional circuit computing it.

Interest in the problem of obtaining lower bounds for the combinational complexity $L(f)$ of natural functions f is mostly stimulated by the fact that such bounds would lead to lower bounds for the Turing complexity of the corresponding languages. To be more exact, let $\{f_n(x_1, x_2, \ldots, x_n)\}_{n=1}^\infty$ be a sequence of Boolean functions and let $\mathfrak{L}$ be a language with alphabet

1980 *Mathematics Subject Classification* (1985 *Revision*). Primary 68Q15, 94C10.

Translation of Proc. Internat. Congr. Math. (Berkeley, Calif., 1986), Vol. 2, Amer. Math. Soc., Providence, R. I., 1987, pp. 1478–1487; MR **89h:** 68072.

$\{0, 1\}$, defined by

$$\varepsilon_1 \varepsilon_2 \cdots \varepsilon_n \in \mathfrak{L} \Leftrightarrow f_n(\varepsilon_1, \varepsilon_2, \ldots, \varepsilon_n) = 1.$$

Then we have the following simple fact, whose exact authorship is apparently quite difficult to establish:

THEOREM 1. *For any Turing machine M that recognizes a language $\mathfrak{L}$,*

$$T_M(n)S_M(n) \succcurlyeq L(f_n),$$

where T_M and S_M denote time and space respectively.

However, notwithstanding considerable efforts, the best lower bounds for $L(f_n)$ for natural functions f_n known today are only linear in n. We note that simple counting arguments show that $L(f_n) \approx 2^n$ for almost all f_n.

While trying to find approaches to obtain lower bounds for the combinational complexity of natural Boolean functions, researchers consider simplified versions. One possible variation is to estimate the *joint complexity* $L(f_1, \ldots, f_m)$ of a collection $\overline{f} = f_1, \ldots, f_m$ of Boolean functions, i.e., the least possible size t of a circuit (1) that computes all the functions in the collection being considered. It is obvious that $L(f_1, \ldots, f_m) \geq m$ if all the f_i's are distinct; thus, as a rule, one restricts oneself to the case $m \preccurlyeq n$ (n is the number of variables). Unfortunately, today there are no nonlinear in n lower bounds even for joint complexity of natural Boolean functions.

Another natural simplification consists of considering only monotone circuits, i.e., circuits in whose construction part b) of the definition (2) is not used. Of course, if a circuit (1) is monotone then all the functions that compose it are also monotone. For a monotone function f, the *monotone complexity* $L^+(f)$ is defined analogously to the combinational one: the only difference is that we consider not all the circuits but only the monotone ones.

Nonlinear lower bounds for joint monotone complexity of natural functions have been known for quite a while. They were first obtained by Nechiporuk [3], who considered collections of monotone functions of the type

$$f_i = \bigvee_{j \in F_i} x_j \qquad (1 \leq i \leq m; \ F_i \subseteq \{1, 2, \ldots, n\}), \tag{3}$$

and proved that

$$\text{if } i_1 \neq i_2 \Rightarrow |F_{i_1} \cap F_{i_2}| \leq 1, \text{ then } L^+(f) \geq \sum_{i=1}^{m} |F_i| - m, \tag{4}$$

and, based on that, presented the explicit example of a system $\overline{f} = f_1, f_2, \ldots,$ f_n of type (3) with $L^+(\overline{f}) \succcurlyeq n^{3/2}$. Collections of type (3) were afterwards named *Boolean sums*. While developing methods of [3] Mehlhorn [18] and Pippenger [21] constructed explicit examples of Boolean sums with the bound

$L^+(\overline{f}) \succeq n^{5/3}$. Nechiporuk's bound (4) was generalized in [25], where Wegener established that if $i_1 \neq i_2 \Rightarrow |F_{i_1} \cap F_{i_2}| \leq k$, then

$$L^+(\overline{f}) \geq k^{-1} \cdot \sum_{i=1}^{m} |F_i| - m.$$

Grigor'ev [2] considered Boolean sums in the case $n = 2^p$, $\{1, 2, \ldots, n\}$ is the set of all the vectors in a p-dimensional vector space over the field F_2, and $\{F_1, F_2, \ldots, F_{n-1}\}$ is the set of all the hyperplanes of this vector space, and proved the bound $L^+(\overline{f}) \succeq n \log n$. Let us note that the methods of the papers just mentioned are inapplicable here.

Monotone symmetric functions or *threshold functions* are defined as follows:

$$T_k^n(x_1, \ldots, x_n) = 1 \Leftrightarrow \sum_{i=1}^{n} x_i \geq k. \tag{5}$$

For them, in [17] the lower bound $L^+(T_1^n, T_2^n, \ldots, T_n^n) \succeq n \log n$ was proved, which asymptotically coincides with the upper bound [8].

Let us now consider *monotone bilinear forms*, i.e., collections of the type

$$f_i = \bigvee_{p, q \in T_i} (x_p \& y_q) \qquad (1 \leq i \leq m; T_i \subseteq [n_1] \times [n_2]). \tag{6}$$

A natural example of such a set is the Boolean multiplication of $m \times m$ matrices $(f_{ij} = \bigvee_{k=1}^{m}(x_{ik} \& y_{kj}), 1 \leq i, j \leq m)$ for which in [22], [20], and [19] the bound $L^+(\overline{f}) \succeq m^3 = n^{3/2}$ was proved.

In [16] a collection (6) is called *semidisjoint* if the following conditions hold:

a) $i_1 \neq i_2 \Rightarrow T_{i_1} \cap T_{i_2} = \varnothing$,

b) $\forall 1 \leq i \leq m \ \forall 1 \leq j \leq n_1 \ (\langle j, k_1 \rangle, \langle j, k_2 \rangle \in T_i \Rightarrow k_1 = k_2)$,

c) $\forall 1 \leq i \leq m \ \forall 1 \leq k \leq n_2 \ (\langle j_1, k \rangle, \langle j_2, k \rangle \in T_i \Rightarrow j_1 = j_2)$.

In [16] for semidisjoint sets (6) the following lower bound was proved:

$$L^+(\overline{f}) \succeq \sum_{i=1}^{m} |T_i| \log |T_i| / \min(n_1, n_2).$$

In particular, this bound for a so-called *convolution*

$$f_k = \bigvee \{(x_p \& y_q) \mid 1 \leq p, q \leq n \text{ and } p + q = k\} \qquad (2 \leq k \leq 2n)$$

is equal to $\Omega(n \log n)$. Weiss proved in [27] that from semidisjointness of a collection (6) the bound $L^+(\overline{f}) \geq \sum_{1}^{n_1} \sqrt{r_j}$ follows, and is stronger in some cases, where r_j is the number of occurrences of x_j in the collection $\overline{f}$. In particular, for convolution he obtained the lower bound $\Omega(n^{3/2})$. Blum [11] proved the weaker bound $\Omega(n^{4/3})$ by other methods.

In [24] Wegener considered collections of functions

$$f_{(\varepsilon_1, \ldots, \varepsilon_{\log_2 n})} = \bigvee_{1 \leq j \leq n/(2 \log_2 n)} \underset{1 \leq i \leq \log_2 n}{\&} x_{\varepsilon_i ij},$$

indexed by sequences $(\varepsilon_1, \varepsilon_2, \ldots, \varepsilon_{\log_2 n})$ of zeros and ones of the set of variables

$$\{x_{\varepsilon ij} \mid 0 \le \varepsilon \le 1, \ 1 \le i \le \log_2 n, \ 1 \le j \le n/(2\log_2 n)\}$$

and proved for them the bound $L^+(\bar{f}) \succeq n^2/(\log^2 n)$, which he improved in [26] to $L^+(\bar{f}) \succeq n^2/\log n$.

Let us now go to monotone complexity of single functions. Among threshold functions the *majority* function $\mathrm{MAJ}(n) = T_{n/2}^n$ stands out. The bound $L^+(\mathrm{MAJ}(n)) \ge 3n$ was obtained for it in [10]; it was improved to $3.5n$ in [13]. It was proved in [12] that $L^+(T_3^n) \ge 2.5n - 5.5$. Tiekenheinrich [23] defined the function $F = T_{n-1}^n \lor (x_{n+1} \ \& \ T_2^n)$ and proved that $L^+(F) \ge 4n - 8$.

Superpolynomial lower bounds for monotone complexity were first obtained by the author in [4] and [5]. The function $\mathrm{CLIQUE}(m, s)$ of the variables $\{x_{ij} \mid 1 \le i < j \le m\}$ is defined in the following way:

$$\mathrm{CLIQUE}(m, s) = \bigvee_{\substack{I \subset [m] \\ |I| = s}} \ \underset{i, j \in I}{\&} x_{ij},$$

and the function $\mathrm{PERM}(m)$ (permanent) of the variables $\{x_{ij} \mid 1 \le i, j \le m\}$ is

$$\mathrm{PERM}(m) = \bigvee_{\sigma \in S_m} \overset{m}{\underset{i=1}{\&}} x_{i\sigma(i)}.$$

Both of these functions have a transparent interpretation in the terminology of graph theory that we shall discuss here. In [4] and [5] the following bounds were proved:

THEOREM 2 [4].
a) $L^+(\mathrm{CLIQUE}(m, s)) = \exp(\Omega(\log^2 m))$ if $s \asymp \log m$.
b) $L^+(\mathrm{CLIQUE}(m, s)) = \Omega(m^s/\log^{2s} m)$ if $s \asymp 1$.

THEOREM 3 [4], [5]. $L^+(\mathrm{PERM}(m)) = \exp(\Omega(\log^2 m))$.

Andreev in [1] introduced the special monotone function $\mathrm{POLY}(q, s)$ of the variables $\{x_{ij} \mid 1 \le i, j \le q\}$ (q is a power of a prime number):

$$\mathrm{POLY}(q, s) = \bigvee \left\{ \overset{q}{\underset{i=1}{\&}} x_{if(i)} \mid f(z) \in \mathrm{GF}(q)[z] \text{ and } \deg(f) \le s - 1 \right\}$$

and showed that methods of [4] and [5] give an exponential bound for it:

THEOREM 4 [1].

$$L^+(\mathrm{POLY}(q, s)) = \exp(\Omega(n^{1/8}/\sqrt{\log n})),$$

if $s \asymp q^{1/4}/\sqrt{\log q}$ ($n = q^2$ is the number of variables).

Soon it became clear that to strengthen bounds up to exponential ones it is not necessary to introduce exotic functions: Alon and Boppana [9] strengthened the bound of Theorem 2 in the following way:

THEOREM 5 [9]. a) *Let* $3 \leq s_1 \leq s_2$ *and* $\sqrt{s_1 s_2} \leq m/(8 \log_2 m)$, *and let a Boolean function* f *be such that* $CLIQUE(m, s_1) \leq f \leq CLIQUE(m, s_2)$. *Then* $L^+(f) = \Omega(\sqrt{s_1})$. *In particular, if* $s_1 = s_2 \asymp (m/8 \log m)^{2/3}$, *then*

$$L^+(CLIQUE(m, s)) = \exp(\Omega(n^{1/6}/\log^{1/3} n)).$$

b) $L^+(CLIQUE(m, s)) = \Omega(m^s/\log^s m)$ *if* $s \asymp 1$.

In addition, Theorem 4 was strengthened in that same paper:

THEOREM 6 [9].

$$L^+(POLY(q, s)) = \exp(\Omega(n^{1/4}\sqrt{\log n})) \quad \text{if } s \asymp \sqrt{q/\log q}.$$

We say a few words about the method by which Theorems 2–6 were obtained. First, the operations $\&$ and $\vee$ in the definition of a circuit (2) are replaced by specially constructed operations $\sqcap$ and $\sqcup$ with the property that from variables $x_1, x_2, \ldots, x_n$ by applying $\sqcap$ and $\sqcup$ one does not obtain all the monotone Boolean functions but only the functions in some special class $\mathfrak{M}$. We also have $f \sqcup g \geq f \vee g$ and $f \sqcap g \leq f \& g$ $(f, g \in \mathfrak{M})$.

Second, the numerical differences of $\sqcap, \sqcup$ from $\&, \vee$ are introduced in the following way:

$$\delta_+ = \max_{f, g \in \mathfrak{M}} |\{\varepsilon \in E_+|(f \& g)(\varepsilon) = 1 \text{ and } (f \sqcap g)(\varepsilon) = 0\}|,$$

$$\delta_- = \max_{f, g \in \mathfrak{M}} P[(f \sqcup g)(\varepsilon^*) = 1 \text{ and } (f \vee g)(\varepsilon^*) = 0],$$

where

$$E_+ = \{\varepsilon \in \{0, 1\}^n \mid F(\varepsilon) = 1 \text{ and } \forall \delta < \varepsilon \ (F(\delta) = 0)\}$$

(F is the monotone function whose complexity we want to estimate) and ε^* is some random variable distributed on $\{0, 1\}^n$.

It is easy to prove the following statement: for any monotone function f there exists $\hat{f} \in \mathfrak{M}$ such that

$$|\{\varepsilon \in E_+|\hat{f}(\varepsilon) = 0 \text{ and } f(\varepsilon) = 1\}| \leq \delta_+ \cdot L^+(f),$$
$$P[\hat{f}(\varepsilon^*) = 1 \text{ and } f(\varepsilon^*) = 0] \leq \delta_- \cdot L^+(f). \tag{7}$$

To obtain $\hat{f}$ it is enough to take a monotone circuit of the minimal size that computes f and to replace the operations $\&$ and $\vee$ by $\sqcap$ and $\sqcup$ in it.

With the right choice of $\mathfrak{M}$, $\sqcup$, $\sqcap$, and ε^* one can obtain Theorems 2–6. However, all of these constructions possess a number of common traits, which we will now note.

The construction of $\mathfrak{M}$ is based first of all on a set $\mathfrak{A}$ consisting of some conjunctions of variables. The number r is fixed, and on $\mathfrak{A}$ the rule of inference is defined in the following way:

$$\mathfrak{K}_1, \mathfrak{K}_2, \ldots, \mathfrak{K}_\tau \vdash \mathfrak{K} \Leftrightarrow \forall i, j \ (1 \leq i < j \leq r \Rightarrow \mathfrak{K}_i \cap \mathfrak{K}_j \subseteq \mathfrak{K}).$$

(here by conjunction we understand just the set of variables occurring in it). A subset $\mathfrak{A}_0 \subseteq \mathfrak{A}$ is called *closed* if it is closed with respect to the rule $\vdash$. $\mathfrak{M}$

consists of all functions of the type $\ulcorner\mathfrak{A}_0\urcorner = \{\bigvee \mathfrak{K} \mid \mathfrak{K} \in \mathfrak{A}_0\}$, where $\mathfrak{A}_0$ ranges over all the closed subsets of $\mathfrak{A}$. To find $f \sqcup g$ for $f = \ulcorner\mathfrak{A}_1\urcorner$ and $g = \ulcorner\mathfrak{A}_2\urcorner$, one has to take

$$f \vee g = \ulcorner\mathfrak{A}_1 \cup \mathfrak{A}_2\urcorner, \tag{8}$$

and add as disjunctive terms all the new conjunctions $\mathfrak{K} \in \mathfrak{A}$ that can be possibly inferred from $\mathfrak{A}_1 \cup \mathfrak{A}_2$. To compute $f \sqcap g$, one has to write down

$$f \,\&\, g = \bigvee_{\mathfrak{K}\in\mathfrak{A}_1} \bigvee_{\mathfrak{L}\in\mathfrak{A}_2} (\mathfrak{K} \,\&\, \mathfrak{L}), \tag{9}$$

and remove all the conjunctive terms $\mathfrak{K} \,\&\, \mathfrak{L}$ that are not in $\mathfrak{A}$ (it is easy to check that the set of remaining conjunctions is closed). The construction of a random variable ε^* depends on the specific case.

In the use of (7) the main roles are played by the following two combinatorial assertions:

if $s = \max_{\mathfrak{K}\in\mathfrak{A}} |\mathfrak{K}|$ then any closed $\mathfrak{A}_0 \subseteq \mathfrak{A}$ contains

no more than $(r - 1)^s$ minimal conjunctions; $\tag{10}$

if $\mathfrak{K}_1, \mathfrak{K}_2, \ldots, \mathfrak{K}_r \in \mathfrak{A}$ are disjoint conjunctions,

then $P[\forall i\ (1 \le i \le r)\ \mathfrak{K}_i(\varepsilon^*) = 0]$ is small. $\tag{11}$

In [9] it is proved that the bound $(r - 1)^s$ in (10) is exact.

EXAMPLE. In the proof of Theorem 3 one should take $\mathfrak{A} = \{x_{i_1 j_1} \,\&\, x_{i_2 j_2} \,\&\, \cdots \,\&\, x_{i_l j_l} \mid l \le s;\ i_1, \ldots, i_l$ pairwise distinct; $j_1, j_2, \ldots, j_l$ pairwise distinct$\}$, where $s = \frac{1}{8}\log_2 m$;

$$E_+ = \{\varepsilon(\sigma) \mid \sigma \in S_m\}, \quad \text{where } \varepsilon_{ij}(\sigma) = 1 \Leftrightarrow j = \sigma(i);$$
$$\varepsilon_{ij}^* = 1 \Leftrightarrow h^*(v_i) = h^*(w_j),$$

where h^* is a function uniformly distributed on $\{0, 1\}^{\{v_1, \ldots, v_m, w_1, \ldots, w_m\}}$;

$$\delta_+ \le (s!r^3)^2 \cdot (m - s - 1)! \quad \text{(Lemma 3 in [5])},$$

$$\delta_- \le (1 - 2^{-s})^{\sqrt{r}/s} \cdot \sum_{i=0}^{s} \left(i! \binom{m}{i}^2\right) \quad \text{(Lemma 6 in [5])},$$

where $r = [m^{1/4}(\log_2 m)^8]$.

Andreev [1] used a different notation; thus for the convenience of the reader we give its possible translation in the language of [4], [5], and [9] (see also the proof of Theorem 6 in [9]). A function which corresponds by operations $\sqcap$ and $\sqcup$ to any pair of functions h_1, h_2 is h_5 in the proof of Lemma 2 of [1]. The class $\mathfrak{M}$ in our notation is the class $\mathfrak{N}_{r,u}^n$ (the definition is on the first page of [1]). The distribution of ε^* is given by the formula ([1], p. 1034 (English 530)) $P[\varepsilon^* = \tilde{\alpha}] = p^{n-\|\tilde{\alpha}\|}(1-p)^{\|\tilde{\alpha}\|}$. The bound $\delta_+ \le (u!r^u)^2$ of Andreev is given by (6) in [1], and the bound $\delta_- \le (up)^r(r^u u!)^2$ by (15) in [1]. The function $\hat{f}$ is the function g_s in the proof of Theorem 1 in [1], and the intermediate functions $g_1, g_2, \ldots, g_s$ in the same proof are exactly the functions in a circuit (1), in which the change of operations $\&, \vee \to \sqcap, \sqcup$ was done. The set $\mathfrak{A}$ in Andreev's paper consists of all the conjunctions of length $\leq u$, and the application of the rule of inference corresponds to the replacement of the (s, r)-regular function g by $x_1 \cdot x_2 \cdots x_s$ in the proof of Lemma 1 in [1]. Property (10) is proved there also. In the proof of Lemma 2 of [1] formulas (8) and (9) take the form $h_1 * h_2 = h_3 \vee h_4$, where h_3 is the family of all the conjunctions that are not in $\mathfrak{A}$ and h_4 is the family of those in $\mathfrak{A}$ $(h_3 = \varnothing$ if $* = \vee)$.

Taking the closure in case (8) is done by going from h_4 to h_5 in formula (4) in [1]. Finally, in the proof of Lemma 1 of [1] the formula $\rho_p(1, g_1) \leq (up)^r$ corresponds to property (11).

In what direction can the results of [4], [5], [1], and [9] develop further? The most interesting question is, of course, how useful they are for obtaining lower bounds over a complete basis. Back in 1973 Schnorr noted that $P \neq NP$ would follow from the following two assertions:

a) for any monotone function f we have $L^+(f) \preccurlyeq p(L(f))$, where $p(t)$ is a fixed polynomial; and

b) $L^+(\text{CLIQUE}(m, m/2))$ grows superpolynomially in m.

But hypothesis a) is rejected by Theorem 3, while b) follows from Theorems 2 and 5. Let us introduce the function

$$I(t) = \max\{L^+(f) \mid L(f) \leq t\},$$

where the maximum is over all the monotone Boolean functions. Then from Theorem 3 it follows that $I(t) = \exp(\Omega(\log^2 t))$. Let us note that if one succeeds in proving the inequality

$$\forall \varepsilon > 0 \; I(t) = O(\exp(t^\varepsilon)), \tag{12}$$

then any one of Theorems 4–6 would lead to $P \neq NP$. However, inequality (12) looks extremely improbable, and we state the following problem.

PROBLEM 1. Disprove (12). [1]

A natural approach to this problem is to strengthen Theorem 3 or to prove an exponential lower bound for monotone complexity of any other sequence of monotone Boolean functions from class P.

With respect to the methods considered above, the author expresses hope that the idea of replacing basic operations by auxiliary ones "slightly different" from them could become useful for consideration of circuits over a complete basis; indirect justification of this is the fresh result formulated below from [6]. However, the combinatorial techniques developed above are apparently not transferable to the nonmonotone case.

Now let us note that Theorems 2b) and 5b) give examples of sequences of monotone functions whose monotone complexity is nonlinear but is bounded

---

[1] *Author's note.* Inequality (12) was recently disproved by É. Tardos [29].

from above by a polynomial. It would be interesting to construct more natural examples of such functions. In particular, we state the following two problems:

PROBLEM 2. Is it true that $L^+(\text{MAJ}(n)) \asymp n \log n$?

PROBLEM 3. Construct explicit examples of monotone bilinear forms consisting of one function with nonlinear lower bound for monotone complexity.

A satisfactory answer to the following question could become the final chord in the study of monotone complexity:

PROBLEM 4. Construct a transparent criterion for the application of the method described above, under which functions from Theorems 2–6 should fall.

On the whole, apparently, it makes sense to switch attention to other possible restrictions on functional circuits.

To conclude this report we will very briefly touch upon results on bounded depth. The definition of the depth k of a circuit is given by induction on k. A *circuit of depth* 0 is an element of the set $\{x_1, \neg x_1, x_2, \neg x_2, \ldots, x_n, \neg x_n\}$. A *circuit of depth* k is a nonempty set of circuits of depth $k - 1$. The size of a circuit C is the cardinality of the transitive reflexive closure of the set C, i.e., the number of circuits used in the construction of C. For a circuit C of depth k, the Boolean function f_C is defined by induction on k. If $k = 0$, then $f_C = C$. The function which is realized by a circuit C of depth $k > 0$ is

$$f_C = \underset{B \in C}{*} f_B, \tag{13}$$

where $* = \bigvee$ if k is even, and $* = \&$ if k is odd. The least possible size of a circuit of depth $k \geq 2$ realizing a function f is denoted by $L_k(f)$. Let us note that for any circuit of depth k and size t one constructs in the obvious way the functional circuit (1) of size $O(kt^2)$ computing the same function; so $L(f) \preccurlyeq k L_k^2(f)$.

In [14], [7], [28], and [15] the function of addition mod 2 (parity) $x_1 \oplus x_2 \oplus \cdots \oplus x_n$ was considered, and, for any fixed k, first a superpolynomial lower bound for $L_k(x_1 \oplus x_2 \oplus \cdots \oplus x_n)$ was proved [14] and [7], and then an exponential one:

THEOREM 7 [28]. $L_k(x_1 \oplus \cdots \oplus x_n) = \exp(\Omega(n^{\lambda_k}))$, $k = \text{const}$.

In [6] the class of circuits of bounded depth was widened in the following way: in the definition of circuit in (13) one more new operation $* = \oplus$ is allowed, and the order in which operations $\{\&, \vee, \oplus\}$ are applied can be arbitrary. We will denote by $L_k^\oplus$ the complexity modified in this way. The following is true:

THEOREM 8 [6]. $L_k^\oplus(\text{MAJ}(n)) = \exp(\Omega(n^{\lambda_k}))$, $k = \text{const}$.

We note that the first step in the proof of Theorem 8, as for monotone complexity, consists in the replacement of basic operations by "slightly different" auxiliary operations analogously to the way $\&$ and $\bigvee$ were replaced by $\sqcap$ and $\sqcup$ in [4], [6], [1], and [9].

BIBLIOGRAPHY

1. A. E. Andreev, *On a method for obtaining lower bounds for the complexity of individual monotone functions*, Dokl. Akad. Nauk SSSR **282** (1985), 1033–1037; English transl. in Soviet Math. Dokl. **31** (1985).

2. D. Yu. Grigor'ev, *A lower bound for the complexity of computation of a family of disjunctions in a monotone basis*, Zap. Nauchn. Sem. Leningrad. Otdel. Mat. Inst. Steklov. (LOMI) **68** (1977), 19–25; English transl. in J. Soviet Math. **15** (1981), no. 1.

3. È. I. Nechiporuk, *On a Boolean matrix*, Problemy Kibernet. Vyp. 21 (1970), 237–240; English transl. in Systems Theory Res. **21** (1970).

4. A. A. Razborov, *Lower bounds for the monotone complexity of some Boolean functions*, Dokl. Akad. Nauk SSSR **281** (1985), 798–801; English transl. in Soviet Math. Dokl. **31** (1985).

5. ___, *Lower bounds of monotone complexity of the logical permanent function*, Mat. Zametki **37** (1985), 387–400; English transl. in Math. Notes **37** (1985).

6. ___, *Lower bounds for the size of circuits of bounded depth over the basis* $\{\&, \oplus\}$, Preprint, Steklov Math. Inst., Acad. Sci. USSR, Moscow, 1986. (Russian) R. Zh. Mat. 1986, 8Γ56. See also *Lower bounds on the dimension of circuits of bounded depth over a complete basis containing the logical addition function*, Mat. Zametki **41** (1987), 598–607; English transl. in Math. Notes **41** (1987).

7. M. Ajtai, Σ_1^1*-formulae on finite structures*, Ann. Pure Appl. Logic **24** (1983), 1–48.

8. M. Ajtai, J. Komlós, and E. Szemerédi, *An* $O(n \log n)$ *sorting network*, Proc. Fifteenth Annual ACM Sympos. Theory of Computing, ACM, New York, 1983, pp. 1–9.

9. N. Alon and R. B. Boppana, *The monotone circuit complexity of Boolean functions*, Preprint, 1985. See also Combinatorica **7** (1987), 1–22.

10. Peter Anthony Bloniarz, *The complexity of monotone Boolean functions and an algorithm for finding shortest paths in a graph*, Ph.D. thesis, M.I.T., Cambridge, Mass., 1977; rev. version, Tech. Rep. No. 238, Laboratory for Computer Sci., M.I.T., Cambridge, Mass., 1979.

11. Norbert Blum, *An* $\Omega(n^{4/3})$ *lower bound on the monotone network complexity of the nth degree convolution*, Theoret. Computer Sci. **36** (1985), 59–69.

12. Paul E. Dunne, *A 2.5n lower bound on the monotone network complexity of* T_3^n, Acta Informatica **22** (1985), 229–240.

13. ___, *Lower bounds on the monotone network complexity of threshold functions*, Proc. Twenty-second Annual Allerton Conf. Communication, Control, and Computing, Dept. of Electrical and Computer Engrg., Univ. of Illinois, Urbana, Ill., 1984, pp. 911–920.

14. Merrick Furst, James B. Saxe, and Michael Sipser, *Parity, circuits, and the polynomial-time hierarchy*, Math. Systems Theory **17** (1984), 13–27.

15. Johan Hastad, *Almost optimal lower bounds for small depth circuits*, Proc. Eighteenth Annual ACM Sympos. Theory of Computing, ACM, New York, 1986, pp. 6–20.

16. Edmund A. Lamagna, *The complexity of monotone networks for certain bilinear forms, routing problems, sorting, and merging*, IEEE Trans. Computers **C-28** (1979), 773–782.

17. Edmund A. Lamagna and John E. Savage, *Combinatorial complexity of some monotone functions*, 15th Annual Sympos. Switching and Automata Theory (1974), IEEE Computer Soc., Long Beach, Calif., 1974, pp. 140–144.

18. Kurt Mehlhorn, *Some remarks on Boolean sums*, Acta Informatica **12** (1979), 371–375.

19. K. Mehlhorn and Z. Galil, *Monotone switching circuits and Boolean matrix product*, Computing **16** (1976), 99–111.

20. Michael S. Paterson, *Complexity of monotone networks for Boolean matrix product*, Theoret. Computer Sci. **1** (1975), 13–20.

21. Nicholas Pippenger, *On another Boolean matrix*, Theoret. Computer Sci. **11** (1980), 49–56.

22. Vaughan R. Pratt, *The power of negative thinking in multiplying Boolean matrices*, SIAM J. Computing **4** (1975), 326–330.

23. Jürgen Tiekenheinrich, *A 4n-lower bound on the monotone network complexity of a one-output Boolean function*, Information Processing Letters **18** (1984), 201–202.

24. Ingo Wegener, *Switching functions whose monotone complexity is nearly quadratic*, Theoret. Computer Sci. **9** (1979), 83–97.

25. ___, *A new lower bound on the monotone network complexity of Boolean sums*, Acta Informatica **13** (1980), 109–114.

26. ___, *Boolean functions whose monotone complexity is of size $n^2/\log n$* , Theoret. Computer Sci. **21** (1982), 213–224.

27. Jürgen Weiss, *An $n^{3/2}$ lower bound on the monotone network complexity of the Boolean convolution*, Information and Control **59** (1983), 184–188.

28. Andrew Chi-Chih Yao, *Separating the polynomial-time hierarchy by oracles*, 26th IEEE Sympos. Foundations of Computer Sci., IEEE Computer Sci. Press, Washington, D.C., 1985, pp. 1–10.

29. Éva Tardos, *The gap between monotone and nonmonotone circuit complexity is exponential*, Combinatorica **8** (1988), 141–142.

Steklov Mathematical Institute
   Moscow 117966
USSR

Translated by I. SHEYKEVICH

Amer. Math. Soc. Transl.
(2) Vol. **147**, 1990

Diophantine Equations and the Evolution of Algebra

I. G. BASHMAKOVA

It is an accepted tradition in the history of mathematics to link Diophantine equations to the development of number theory, and the evolution of algebra (at least up to the middle of the 19th century) to the investigation of determinate algebraic equations—above all, to the problem of solving such equations in radicals. This point of view, however, fails to explain what factors conditioned the development of algebra from the third century B.C. to the sixteenth century A.D.—a period that admittedly began with Euclid's complete solution of quadratic equations and ended with the solution of cubic and quartic equations but also witnessed the extension of the domain of numbers to the field $\mathbf{Q}$ of rational numbers and the introduction of literal symbolism, at first for denoting the unknown and its powers and later also for the parameters of a problem. During this period algebra lost its geometric form, and its construction on an arithmetical basis was begun. How is one to explain this, and what motivated all these changes?

We shall try to show that, from the very beginning, the evolution of algebra was conditioned by the investigation not only of determinate but also of *indeterminate*, or *Diophantine*, equations—specifically, Diophantine equations with rational coefficients whose solutions were sought in the field $\mathbf{Q}$ of rational numbers (or just in $\mathbf{Q}^+$, the system of positive rationals). To be sure, no one had as yet formulated the problem of finding all rational solutions of a Diophantine equation, and certainly not the problem of the structure of the set of solutions—it was enough to find one solution, or, if possible, infinitely many.

We encounter the elements of algebra for the first time in ancient Babylon, two thousand years before the Christian era. Many clay tablets, deciphered

1980 *Mathematics Subject Classification* (1985 *Revision*). Primary 11-03, 11D09; Secondary 11D25, 11D41.

Translation of Proc. Internat. Congr. Math. (Berkeley, Calif., 1986), Vol. 2, Amer. Math. Soc., Providence, R.I., 1987, pp. 1612–1628; MR **81f**: 01002.

since the twenties of this century, attest to the high level of Babylonian mathematical culture. The greatest achievement of this period was the solution in radicals of quadratic equations. By this is meant that the Babylonians were able to express the roots of a quadratic equation in terms of its coefficients using the four arithmetical operations and the operation of extraction of square roots.

A few remarks are in order. First, Babylonians had no symbols for unknowns and parameters, and so did not write down general "solution formulas" (as we do) but demonstrated them by means of many numerical examples of the same kind. Second, rather than speak of a "solution formula" it is more accurate to speak of the equivalent *algorithm*, listing the operations to be applied to the coefficients in order to obtain the value of a root of the equation.

It is natural to assume that in order to obtain such an algorithm the Babylonians had to transform equations

$$ax^2 \pm bx = c,$$

or reduce to the form $u^2 = B$ systems

$$x \pm y = a, \qquad xy = b,$$

frequently occurring in their tables. For this they had to know some general properties of the operations of addition and multiplication and to be able to make substitutions. Other examples in the tables confirm this assumption. We can therefore take it for granted that the Babylonians were familiar with the properties and rules that we express by means of the formulas

$$(a \pm b)c = ac \pm bc, \tag{1}$$

$$(a \pm b)^2 = a^2 + b^2 \pm 2ab, \tag{2}$$

$$(a + b)(a - b) = a^2 - b^2. \tag{3}$$

Thus two thousand years before the Christian era the Babylonians knew the properties of some composition laws ((1) is the distributive law of multiplication over addition), made substitutions, and solved by algebraic methods quadratic equations and systems equivalent to such equations. All this justifies saying that the Babylonians knew the elements of algebra. We propose to call this first stage in the evolution of algebra *numerical algebra*.

But even during this very early period the rise and development of algebraic methods was not restricted to the solution of quadratic equations. The solution of indeterminate equations is considered in very early texts. One of the earliest equations of this kind investigated by the Babylonians was the equation

$$x^2 + y^2 = z^2. \tag{4}$$

They looked for its rational solutions and knew how to find solution triples (x, y, z), later known as "Pythagorean triples". While it is not quite clear whether the Babylonians knew the general solution formulas of this equation, they certainly linked "Pythagorean triples" to the solution of the indeterminate equation

$$u^2 + v^2 = 2w^2. \tag{5}$$

Specifically, they established that if (x, y, z) is a solution of (4), then

$$u = x + y, \quad v = x - y, \quad w = z$$

is a solution of (5). What is most remarkable, however, is that knowing a solution (u_0, v_0, w_0) of (5) they were able to find infinitely many of its other solutions (u_n, v_n, w_0). For this they used the formulas (see [7])

$$(p^2 + q^2)(\alpha^2 + \beta^2) = (\alpha p - \beta q)^2 + (\alpha q + \beta p)^2 = (\alpha p + \beta q)^2 + (\alpha q - \beta p)^2, \tag{6}$$

now called the rule of composition of forms of type $x^2 + y^2$. We shall see that this formula played a very important role in the mathematics of peoples in the East and in Europe during the Middle Ages.

The Babylonians established the formulas (6), like other formulas, only for particular numbers. But the ancient calculators realized that the numbers they used could be replaced by other arbitrary rational numbers.

Now let (u_0, v_0, w_0) be a solution of the equation (5). To obtain another solution the Babylonians used the formulas (6) with α and β subject to $\alpha^2 + \beta^2 = 1$ (for example, $\alpha = 3/5$, $\beta = 4/5$), $p = u_0$, and $q = v_0$. Then

$$2w_0^2 = 2w_0^2(\alpha^2 + \beta^2) = (u_0^2 + v_0^2)(\alpha^2 + \beta^2) = (\alpha u_0 - \beta v_0)^2 + (\alpha v_0 + \beta u_0)^2$$
$$= (\alpha u_0 + \beta v_0)^2 + (\alpha v_0 - \beta u_0)^2,$$

that is, they obtained two more solutions

$$u_1 = \alpha u_0 - \beta v_0, \quad v_1 = \alpha v_0 + \beta u_0,$$
$$u_2 = \alpha u_0 + \beta v_0, \quad v_2 = \alpha v_0 - \beta u_0.$$

Using these new values for p and q they obtained new solutions, and so on. As for the choice of values for α and β, such values can be obtained by dividing all terms of a Pythagorean triple $(\bar{x}, \bar{y}, \bar{z})$ by $\bar{z}$.

We see that already in the first stage of its evolution algebra was influenced by problems of solving determinate equations as well as by the investigation and solution of Diophantine equations.

The second stage in the development of algebra coincides with the flowering of Greek mathematics (fifth to second centuries B.C.). It was during this period that mathematical knowledge amassed over centuries was transformed into mathematics in the modern sense—an abstract science based on a system of proofs. Whereas for the Babylonians (who undoubtedly made use of individual deductions) the center of gravity was in *the results* rather than in *the method of obtaining results*, it now shifted to *method and proof.* Also, proof was the means not only of establishing the truth of a proposition but also of explaining its *essence* by uncovering its connection with other propositions—those it is based on as well as those based on it. This aspect of proof was already emphasized by Aristotle in his *Posterior Analytics*.

This radical transformation of our science affected all its branches, including arithmetic and algebra. At the end of the fifth century B.C. were laid the foundations of elementary number theory and the theory of positive rational numbers, viewed as ratios (in modern terms, as pairs of whole numbers) that were not regarded as numbers during the classical period. At first, the foundation of mathematics was arithmetic, which was used to construct the theory of music (harmony), astronomy, and, in part, geometry (the theory of similarity). This was the earliest attempt at arithmetization of mathematics and mathematical physics—an attempt reflected in the winged aphorism of the early Pythagoreans "all is number." The discovery of incommensurable segments (whose ratio is not expressible as a ratio of whole numbers) led to a crisis of the arithmetical conception. Soon geometry came to be viewed as the more general science, and as such it became the foundation and language of the mathematics of antiquity. By the end of the fifth century B.C. algebra too adopted geometric dress. The Greeks translated all arithmetical operations into the language of geometry and began to operate directly with geometric objects—segments, areas, and volumes—without recourse to numbers. Following H. G. Zeuthen, this stage of the evolution of algebra is usually referred to as *geometric algebra*. The primary objects of this algebra were segments. Segments could be added ("set one to another"), and one could subtract a smaller segment from a larger one. The rectangle on two segments was called their product. The product of three segments was represented by the rectangular parallelepiped on these segments. The product of more than three segments was not representable; to speak of such a product made as little sense as speaking of space of four or five dimensions.

In geometric algebra it was possible to prove the properties and identities known already to the Babylonians. In fact, Euclid's *Elements* contains geometric proofs of the formulas (1)–(3). In particular, the formula $(a+b)^2 = a^2+b^2+2ab$ is proved geometrically by considering a square whose side is the sum of the magnitudes a and b (Figure 1). Problems leading to quadratic equations were also formulated geometrically. For example, the

ab	b^2
a^2	ab

FIGURE 1

problem equivalent to the equation $x^2 = ab$ was stated as follows: "Transform a given rectangle (that is, ab) into a square." In his *Elements* Euclid solves the most general quadratic equations $\alpha x(a-x) = S$ and $\alpha x(a+x) = S$ (here α denotes a ratio, a a segment, and S an area), and for the first of them formulates the restriction on α, a, and S that guarantees that the root is real and positive. All proofs are general and apply to commensurable as well as incommensurable magnitudes.

The *Elements* also considers problems that reduce to the successive solution of a number of quadratic equations. Thus to express the edge of a regular dodecahedron in terms of the diameter D of the circumscribed sphere it is necessary to solve a biquadratic equation that is reducible to two quadratic equations. In general, by means of geometric algebra (in other words, using ruler and compass) it is possible to solve any algebraic equation whose roots are expressible by means of real quadratic radicals (or even any algebraic equation that can be reduced to the successive solution of a chain of quadratic equations such that the coefficients of each equation in the chain are rational functions of the roots of its predecessor). Thus the problem of solving determinate equations in radicals appears in the second stage of the evolution of algebra as the problem of solving equations in quadratic radicals. For example, the equations $x^4 + x^3 + \cdots + x + 1 = 0$ and $x^{16} + x^{15} + \cdots + x + 1 = 0$ are solvable by means of geometric algebra, but $x^6 + x^5 + \cdots + x + 1 = 0$ is not. (This was shown by Gauss in his *Disquisitiones arithmeticae* of 1801.)

In the fifth century B.C. there appeared the first "unsolvable" problems, that is, problems unsolvable by means of ruler and compass, such as the famous problem of doubling a cube (equivalent to the equation $x^3 = 2a^3$), and the problem of trisecting an angle. Some cubic equations were investigated and solved by Archimedes. The roots of such cubic equations, including those of the equation of doubling a cube, were found by intersecting hyperbolas and parabolas. Hence the problem of solution of equations in cubic radicals was not posed in antiquity. This is all the more true of the problem of solution of equations in higher-order radicals.

In the theoretical works of the fifth to the third centuries B.C. we encounter two types of indeterminate equations. One is the Pythagorean equation $x^2 + y^2 = z^2$, and the other is the equation

$$y^2 = ax^2 + 1, \tag{7}$$

where a is a nonsquare whole number, subsequently named the Pell-Fermat equation. For both of these equations one tried to find positive integer solutions.

The study of the Pythagorean equation runs all through the mathematics of antiquity. The early Pythagoreans (sixth to fifth centuries B.C.) and Plato (fourth century B.C.) proposed solution formulas for this equation. Its most general solution is found in Euclid's *Elements*, where it is shown that every solution can be represented in the form

$$x^2 = p^2 - q^2, \quad y = 2pq, \quad z = p^2 + q^2, \quad p, q \in \mathbf{Z}^+.$$

Equation (7) for $a = 2$ is also considered in the *Elements*, where it is shown that if x_{n-1}, y_{n-1} is a solution of (7) for $a = 2$, then a new solution x_n, y_n can be obtained by using the formulas $x_n = x_{n-1} + y_{n-1}$ and $y_n = 2x_{n-1} + y_{n-1}$.

The later history of indeterminate equations attests that many other types of indeterminate equations were solved during the classical period, but their investigation remained outside theoretical science and had no effect on geometric algebra.

A third—and very important—stage in the evolution of algebra began during the early centuries A.D. and ended in the late 16th and early 17th century. It was then that algebra acquired its own distinctive language—the literal calculus.

Geometric language hampered the development of algebra—it was not indigenous to it. First, it blocked consideration of products of more than three magnitudes, and thereby also of equations of degree greater than three; and, second, the geometric attire made algebra clumsy and largely nonoperative. Small wonder that, following the decline of classical Greek mathematics in the first century B.C.—which entailed, crucially, a break in the tradition—scholars rejected geometric algebra. True, we encounter geometric proofs of algebraic rules and formulas much later (such proofs still turned up in the 16th century), but algebra itself was no longer imprisoned in geometric armor—it acquired a new form.

The return to numerical algebra is found already in the works of Heron of Alexandria (first century A.D.), who solved numerical quadratic equations as well as interesting new problems involving indeterminate equations. We note that in "Heron's formula" for finding the area of a triangle given its sides, the expression under the square root is a product of four magnitudes. This would have been inadmissible during the classical period. The new tendencies are particularly pronounced in the works of Diophantus of Alexandria (third century A.D.) who laid the foundation of literal algebra.

Only parts of two of Diophantus' works have come down to us. They are (six of the 13 books of) his *Arithmetic* and (excerpts of) his treatise *On polygonal numbers*. Of very much greater interest to us is the first of these.

The *Arithmetic* begins with an introduction that is, essentially, the first exposition of the foundations of algebra. Here Diophantus constructs the field of rational numbers and introduces literal symbolism. We also find here a formulation of rules of operation with polyomials and equations.

Heron had already admitted into mathematics positive rational numbers (in the mathematics of classical antiquity "numbers" are only sets of units, that is, natural numbers). Diophantus took another radical step by introducing negative numbers. It was only then that he obtained a system closed under the four arithmetical operations, that is, a field. Without this step literal algebra could not have evolved. We would now call Diophantus' method of introducing new objects the axiomatic method. Diophantus defines a new object which he calls "want" ($\lambda\varepsilon\tilde{\imath}\psi\iota\varsigma$) by stating the rules of operation with such objects. Specifically, if the symbol $(-)$ characterizes the new objects and $(+)$ an arbitrary positive rational number, then Diophantus postulates:

$$(-)\cdot(-)=(+), \qquad (-)\cdot(+)=(-).$$

He does not formulate the rules of addition and subtraction of the new numbers, but he applies them freely in his writings. It is conceivable that these operations were used before his time.

Further, Diophantus introduced an unknown number which is denoted by the special symbol ς, as well as its first six positive and six negative powers. He thus broke completely with geometric algebra in which powers higher than the third were not representable. It is remarkable that Diophantus also introduced a symbol for the zeroth power of the unknown and singled out two rules that correspond to two of the axioms defining a group:

$$x^m \cdot 1 = x^m, \qquad x^m \cdot x^{-m} = 1.$$

For products of other powers of the unknown Diophantus set down a "multiplication table" that we could now write down briefly as

$$x^m x^n = x^{m+n}, \qquad -6 \le m + n \le 6.$$

Finally, he introduced symbols for the minus sign and for the equality sign.

All this enabled Diophantus to write down the conditions of a problem in the form of an equation or a system of equations. Strictly speaking, up to the time of Diophantus there were neither determinate nor indeterminate equations. There were only problems that could be reduced to equations.

In the introduction Diophantus formulated two basic rules of operating with equations. They were: (1) the rule of transfer of a term of an equation from one side to the other (with change of sign) and (2) the rule of collecting similar terms. These are the very same rules that later became widely known under the Arabic names of "al jabr" and "al-mu-kabala." Also, Diophantus made most ingenious use of the rule of substitution, without formulating it.

Thus in Diophantus' books we find clear-cut equations and purely algebraic transformations. But what do these books deal with? What problems did Diophantus wish to investigate and solve when he introduced his symbolism and extended the domain of numbers? In other words, what problems spurred the birth of literal symbolism? The core of the *Arithmetic* is the solution in rational numbers of *indeterminate equations and systems*, and it actually includes equations of the sixth degree. As for determinate equations, Diophantus solved linear and quadratic equations with rational roots. No powers of the unknown higher than the second were needed to write down these equations and their solutions. Thus it was obviously not the problem of solving determinate equations that impelled Diophantus to make innovations in algebra!

We shall now consider the possibilities and bounds of Diophantus' symbolism. Usually, Diophantus' equations contain several—at any rate, not less than two—unknowns, and yet Diophantus introduced symbols for just one unknown and its powers. How, then, did he manage to solve problems?

Each problem was formulated in general terms; for example, the statement of Problem 8 in Book II is "Decompose a square into a sum of squares." Then all parameters were assigned concrete numerical values; in the example just quoted the given square is 16. Then Diophantus chose the primary unknown, which he denoted by his special symbol, and expressed the remaining unknowns as linear, quadratic, or more complex rational functions of the primary unknown and the parameters. In the above example, the second unknown is expressed in terms of the primary one (t) as $kt - a$. Here a is taken as 4 (the square root of 16) and the coefficient of t is taken to be any rational number; while putting it equal to 2 Diophantus stipulates that one could have chosen for it any other number. The scheme just described is the simplest. At times, the choice of parameters must be restricted; for example, it may be necessary to choose a whole number that is representable as a sum of two or three squares. Then Diophantus analyzes the problem and determines from what set M of numbers it is possible to select one or another parameter. Thus the concrete numbers play a double role, as ordinary numbers and as signs for arbitrary parameters. We find this second function in algebra until the end of the sixteenth century.

Finally, in the course of solving a problem Diophantus may, successively, denote different unknowns by the same symbol (he sometimes applies such "renaming" three to four times). Thus during this period in the evolution of algebra the very process of denoting the unknowns called for great skill.

To sum up: Diophantus was the first to systematically reduce indeterminate and determinate problems to equations. One could say that he did for a large class of problems in arithmetic and algebra what Descartes later did for a large class of problems in geometry, namely he reduced them to the formulation and solution of algebraic equations. Indeed, in order to solve a problem—an arithmetical one in the case of Diophantus, a geometric one in the case of Descartes—both formulated an algebraic equation which they transformed and investigated in accordance with the rules of algebra. The transformations involved (elimination of unknowns, collection of similar terms, various substitutions) had no immediate arithmetical (in the case of Diophantus) or geometric (in the case of Descartes) significance. Only the final result of these formal calculations was given a relevant interpretation and yielded the solution of the problem in question. We are used to linking this important step to Descartes' creation of analytic geometry, but in fact it was taken very much earlier by Diophantus in his *Arithmetic*. It is remarkable that before they became familiar with Diophantus' *Arithmetic*, none of the European scholars of the 13th to 16th centuries entertained the idea of applying algebra to solve number-theoretic problems.

For Diophantus himself the central problem was the investigation and solution of indeterminate equations. The genesis of literal algebra is linked to these very equations.

We note that Diophantus found basic methods for obtaining rational solutions of a quadratic equation in two unknowns

$$F_2(x, y) = 0$$

for which one knows one rational solution. Diophantus employed even more sophisticated and interesting methods to find rational solutions of indeterminate third and fourth degree equations in two unknowns. We can trace the history of these methods all the way to the works of Henri Poincaré, written at the beginning of this century, in which he relies on these very methods to construct the arithmetic of algebraic curves.

The further progress of algebra right up to the 10th and 11th centuries was also tied to indeterminate equations. At the beginning of the 10th century four books of arithmetic attributed to Diophantus were translated into Arabic. These books are largely devoted to Diophantine equations and were apparently written in the fourth and fifth centuries, in Alexandria. They contain original problems, which may be attributed to Diophantus, as well as commentaries on these problems. In these books there appear the eighth and ninth powers of the unknown.

Indeterminate equations occupy a significant place in the algebraic treatises of Abū Kāmil (beginning of the 10th century) and al-Karaji (about 1100). Both applied the same methods of investigation and solution of equations as Diophantus (except for the solution of indeterminate cubic equations, whose method of solution was unknown to them). In his book *Al-Fahri*, al-Karaji transformed Diophantus' short algebraic introduction into a large treatise on algebra. Here he introduces infinitely many positive and infinitely many negative powers of the unknown and defines the rules of operation with them. For negative numbers al-Karaji formulates not only the rules of multiplication—as Diophantus did—but also the rules of addition and subtraction. In this treatise al-Karaji essentially defines algebra as the science of solution of equations *without differentiating between determinate and indeterminate equations*; his solutions alternate between the two types (but there are more determinate equations in his work than in Diophantus').

Later (in the 11th century) Omar Khayyam investigated cubic equations. He found their roots as the abscissas of points of intersection of conic sections. Traditionally, Muslim mathematicians gave not only the "numerical" solution of a quadratic equation but also its geometric justification. But al-Karaji also gives a purely algebraic justification based on completing the square; he refers to this method as "the solution according to Diophantus".

The one fundamental deviation of Muslim mathematicians from Diophantus' principles was their rejection of algebraic symbolism. They used special terms to denote the unknown and its powers.

In Europe the advances in algebra come between the 13th and 16th centuries. The algebraic tradition was transmitted along two routes, one from the Muslim East and the other from Byzantium. The first eminent mathematician was Leonardo Pisano, or Fibonacci (13th century). In his famous *Liber abaci* (1202) he introduced decimal positional notation and solved systems of linear equations as well as quadratic equations. We also owe to Fibonacci a profound analysis of indeterminate equations presented in his *Liber quadratorum* (1225). To give the reader some notion of these investigations it suffices to recall that Fibonacci was the first to claim—four centuries before Fermat—that the area of a right triangle with rational sides cannot be a square. This proposition is equivalent to Fermat's Last Theorem for the case $n = 4$. But in dealing with indeterminate problems Fibonacci did not use algebraic methods; rather, he solved them purely arithmetically. The same can be said of Luca Pacioli's *Summa de arithmetica, geometria, proportioni et proportionalita* (published in 1494 in Venice), an encyclopedia of the mathematical knowledge of its time. There we find for the first time a statement of the problem of solution in radicals of equations of third and higher degrees. Pacioli considered these problems, like the problem of squaring the circle, to be unsolvable.

At the time of the publication of Pacioli's *Summa*, European mathematicians were making extensive use of symbols for denoting the unknown and its positive powers as well as for denoting the operations of addition, subtraction, multiplication, and extraction of roots. True, in this they adopted the Byzantine method of denoting powers, which was far less convenient than Diophantus'. It was based on the multiplicative principle: the "quadrato-cube" denoted the sixth power (rather than the fifth, as for Diophantus), the fifth power was denoted by $p^\circ r^\circ$, *primo relato* (that is, "first undescribed"), the seventh power was denoted by $2^\circ r^\circ$, *secundo relato* ("second undescribed"), the ninth power was called "cubo-cube," and so on. The *Summa* contains a table of such designations. But up to the end of the 16th century there were symbols neither for a second unknown nor, predictably, for parameters.

Signal advances in algebra came in the 16th century. The most important of these were (1) the solution in radicals of cubic and quartic equations, (2) the introduction of complex numbers, and (3) the creation of a literal calculus.

Thus the problem of solving an equation in radicals turned up in the 16th century after a break of more than 30 centuries! All that time, it was essentially indeterminate equations that were the source of stimulating impulses. We shall describe their effect on algebra in the 16th century.

We shall not give the dramatic history of the solution of the cubic equation; that history is given in all books on the history of mathematics. We will, however, quote H. G. Zeuthen's estimate of this breakthrough:

> Thus what is involved here is not the invention of a method but the discovery—yes, the discovery—of the form of irrationality of the roots of the equations in question. [3].

And what was the immediate effect of this discovery on the development of algebra? In the first place, its *psychological* importance was immense. It showed that "the ancients did not know everything," it strengthened European scholars' faith in their own powers, and gave them the courage to make further gains. Soon the further investigation of the equation

$$x^3 = px + q, \qquad p > 0, \; q > 0, \tag{8}$$

whose solution is given by the formula

$$x = \sqrt[3]{q/2 + \sqrt{(q/2)^2 - (p/3)^3}} + \sqrt[3]{q/2 - \sqrt{(q/2)^2 - (p/3)^3}}, \tag{9}$$

provided the opportunity to use this courage. Indeed, if $(q/2)^2 < (p/3)^3$, then under the square root sign in (9) we have the negative expression $(q/2)^2 - (p/3)^3$. On the other hand, it was not possible to impose the restriction $(q/2)^2 \geq (p/3)^3$ because for $(q/2)^2 < (p/3)^3$ the equation (8) has real roots. A relevant example known to 16th-century mathematicians was the equation $x^3 = 15x + 4$ with root $x = 4$ (and two other roots that also are real). This was called the "irreducible case." Neither Tartaglia, nor Cardano, to whom we owe the solution of the general cubic, succeeded in solving the riddle of the "irreducible case." Its riddle was solved by Raphael Bombelli, one of the most eminent of Renaissance mathematicians. But he could do this only after a profound study of Diophantus' *Arithmetic*.

We have come to the most important—but usually underestimated—event in the history of Renaissance algebra, namely the introduction of European mathematicians to Diophantus' *Arithmetic*. Study of this remarkable work, and familiarization with Diophantus' methods, led to a decisive turn in the development of algebra. At first 143 (of the 189) problems in the *Arithmetic* appeared in Bombelli's *Algebra* (1572) [6]. But what mattered was not just this "inclusion" of the problems. The historian of science E. Bortolotti, who studied the manuscripts in Bombelli's *Nachlass*, observed that, after he got to know the *Arithmetic*, Bombelli's style underwent a complete change. Problems with "circumstances" in the form of pretty stories of a pseudopractical nature were replaced by problems stated in a dry mathematical manner; the notations for the powers of the unknown were changed in the spirit of Diophantus; and, finally, new objects—negative and complex numbers—were introduced by means of Diophantus' method. Bombelli introduced negative numbers by defining for them rules of addition, subtraction, multiplication, and division. Then he took the next—and remarkably bold—step of introducing in a similar manner complex numbers! If we eschew unfamiliar notation and use the now common symbol i for the imaginary unit, Bombelli's rules of multiplication can be written as

$$1 \cdot i = i, \quad i \cdot i = -1, \quad -1 \cdot i = -i, \quad -i \cdot i = 1.$$

We see that Bombelli grasped the essence of the method of introduction of new mathematical objects and applied it brilliantly.

After introducing the imaginary unit i, Bombelli considered expressions of the form $a + bi$ added and subtracted "coordinatewise"; that is,

$$(a + bi) \pm (c + di) = a \pm c + (b \pm d)i,$$

and multiplied according to the rule of multiplication of polynomials. As Bourbaki put it, "this was the first appearance of the notion of linear independence." Using complex numbers, Bombelli was able to resolve the "irreducible case" of a cubic equation, which until then had baffled all mathematicians. Bombelli's book is undoubtedly a brilliant treatise on algebra.

The third part of his *Algebra* deals with indeterminate equations. Here Bombelli reproduced Diophantus' problems with occasional changes of the numerical parameters and completed many of the problems whose solution was either just sketched by Diophantus or omitted altogether. The solutions show that Bombelli clearly understood Diophantus' methods of dealing with indeterminate equations but made no attempt to generalize them. For example, he was the first to solve Diophantus' equation

$$x^3 + y^3 = a^3 - b^3,$$

but only for $a = 4$, $b = 3$—he did not consider other values of a and b.

In sum, we can say that whereas Bombelli's methods and notation evolved under the influence of Diophantus' *Arithmetic*, his interest was tied to the problem of solving equations in radicals.

The stage of development of algebra that we are now considering was completed by François Viète (1540–1603), the greatest algebraist of the Renaissance. From the time of Diophantus, mathematicians perfected the notation for the unknown and its powers. Bombelli introduced symbols for arbitrary whole positive powers in the form of a homogeneous sequence $\overset{1}{,} \overset{2}{,} \overset{3}{,} \ldots$. Symbols indicating powers appeared above and to the right of appropriate coefficients; for example, $x^3 + 5x$ was written as $1^3 \tilde{p} 5^1$. Simon Stevin introduced similar notations for the powers of the second and third unknown. But no one thought of introducing notations for arbitrary parameters. With a view to constructing an "analytic art" (Viète's name for algebra that avoided the use of non-Latin words) that would combine the rigor and depth of the geometry of the ancients with the operational effectiveness of algebra and leave no unsolved problems (*nullum non problema solvere*), Viète constructed the first literal calculus. Specifically, he proposed to denote unknowns by vowels and known arbitrary magnitudes (parameters) by consonants. By further adopting the classical symbols $+$ and $-$ for the respective operations of addition and multiplication, and, above all, by adopting the rule of opening parentheses and the rule of replacing an arbitrary letter with an expression obtained from letters by means of the rules of operations, he was able to *write down and derive formulas*. It is difficult for us to imagine that up to the time of Viète *mathematics functioned without formulas*, that all calculations which we now carry out *in a purely mechanical manner* had to be "done in the head." This is indeed so. We owe it to Viète that we can now replace certain arguments with calculations.

Viète's calculus differed from that of present-day algebra in that, following the principles of geometric algebra, he took into consideration dimensions of magnitudes: addition and subtraction could only be applied to magnitudes of the same dimensions, and multiplication and division of magnitudes involved addition and subtraction of their respective dimensions. We owe the modern form of the literal calculus to René Descartes (1596–1650).

Turning to the works of Viète, we see that he applied his calculus primarily to treating Diophantine equations. In his *Zetetics* (mainly in Books IV and V) he systematically algebraized the methods of Diophantus and generalized many of his problems. It is striking that Viète, like Bombelli, introduced a calculus of new objects, specifically, a calculus of triangles equivalent to the multiplication of complex numbers. Viète's calculus of triangles was based on the composition formula (6) and was called *genesis triangulorum*.

Let there be given two right triangles with respective sides B, D, Z and F, G, H, where the first letter denotes the base and the last one the hypotenuse (Figure 2). The hypotenuse of the resultant triangle is required to

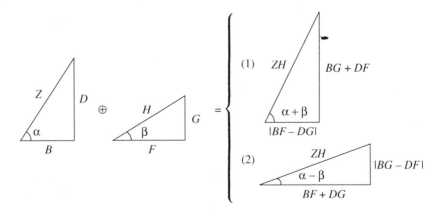

FIGURE 2

be equal to the product ZH of the hypotenuses of the component triangles, and its legs are to be rationally expressible in terms of their respective legs. Now by (6),

$$Z^2 H^2 = (B^2 + D^2)(F^2 + G^2) = (BF - DG)^2 + (BG + DF)^2$$
$$= (BF + DG)^2 + (BG - DF)^2.$$

In other words, the composition yields two right triangles with respective sides $|BF - DG|$, $BG + DF$, ZH and $BF + DG$, $|BG - DF|$, ZH. Viète notes that the acute angle at the base of the first triangle is equal to the sum of the base angles of the component triangles, and the corresponding angle in the second triangle is equal to their difference. If we associate with each triangle a complex number, the number $B + Di$ with the first triangle and the number $F + Gi$ with the second, then the first composition triangle corresponds to the product $(B + Di)(F + Gi)$ and the second to the product $(B + Di)(F - Gi)$; here $F - Gi$ is the complex conjugate of $F + Gi$. But the latter triangles can also be described in terms of their respective hypotenuses and acute base angles. If we write the first component triangle as (Z, α), where α is the acute base angle, and the second as (H, β), then the first composition triangle is $(ZH, \alpha + \beta)$ and the second is $(ZH, \alpha - \beta)$. Thus Viète's calculus makes immediately clear the most important property of complex numbers, namely that under multiplication the absolute values of complex numbers multiply and their arguments add. Viète also composed the first triangle with itself and then, successively, with the triangles obtained by composition. In this way he obtained the series of triangles $(Z^2, 2\alpha)$, $(Z^3, 3\alpha)$, and so on. This enabled him to deduce the formula

$$[z(\cos \varphi + i \sin \varphi)]^m = z^m (\cos m\varphi + i \sin m\varphi),$$

later named after de Moivre. By means of this formula Viète expressed the sines and cosines of multiple arcs as polynomials in sines and cosines.

Let us compare the complex-number symbols of Bombelli and the triangle calculus of Viète. Both systems had advantages and disadvantages. Bombelli's number symbols were convenient for carrying out the four arithmetical operations; in modern terms, they formed a field, that is, the two laws of composition defined for them had the same "good" properties as addition and multiplication of rational numbers. But they had no "trigonometric (= polar) form"; that is, there was no connection between them and the notions of argument and absolute value. This meant that the operation of root extraction was not readily applicable to them, and they could not be conveniently applied in trigonometry. Viète's calculus of triangles admitted an algebraic as well as trigonometric interpretation and was therefore immediately applied to obtain the key trigonometric formulas. Viète used it to solve indeterminate equations. But this calculus involved just one operation (corresponding to multiplication) defined for triangles; it was thus constructed in the spirit of the mathematics of antiquity. That is why, during the subsequent development of Renaissance mathematics, the preferred system was Bombelli's system of number symbols. In the 18th century these symbols were given a trigonometric interpretation and in the 19th century, largely as a result of Gauss's introduction of the arithmetic of complex numbers, they acquired complete legitimacy.

Thus throughout the third stage in the evolution of algebra, problems of Diophantine analysis played a fundamental role, and it was only at the end of this stage that investigation of determinate equations acquired a marked influence.

The fourth stage in the history of algebra began in the 1630s and lasted until the 1770s. During that time mathematicians tried hard to solve in radicals equations of the fifth and higher degrees. Attempts were made by Euler, Bézout, Waring, and many others. At the same time, the fundamental theorem of algebra, which asserts that a polynomial with real coefficients can be written as a product of linear and quadratic factors, began to attract attention. Proofs of this theorem were given by d'Alembert, Euler, Lagrange, Laplace, and, finally, Gauss. In this connection there developed the study of groups of substitutions, of symmetric functions, and of rational functions of the roots of an equation invariant under various permutations of the roots. All this prepared the ground for the future theory of Galois. By tradition, Diophantine equations were still studied in algebra (all of the second volume of Euler's *Introduction to algebra* was devoted to indeterminate analysis) but, due to the works of Fermat and Euler, they became amalgamated with number theory. From that time on it is difficult to separate stimuli due to indeterminate equations as such from stimuli generated by number theory. Perhaps the only exception is Fermat's Last Theorem. Already its proof for the case $n = 3$ required the extension of the notion of integer from that of rational integers to numbers of the form $a + b\sqrt{-3}$, where a and b are rational integers.

The fifth stage in the evolution of algebra—from about 1770 to about 1870—was, apparently, dominated by the problem of solving equations in radicals. It suffices to mention the fundamental researches of Lagrange, Gauss, Abel, and Galois, that resulted in the introduction of such fundamental concepts as field, group, normal subgroup, solvable group, and so on. But even here there is a second line of development connected with Fermat's Last Theorem, the theory of quadratic forms and the reciprocity laws. To study these problems it was necessary to extend the notion of a rational integer to that of an algebraic integer, and to construct the arithmetic of the field of algebraic numbers—a development that led to the introduction of the notions of ring, module, and ideal. All these notions are of fundamental significance in modern algebra, and find applications beyond its borders.

After the 1870s the problem of solving equations in radicals lost its former significance. Algebra was gradually transformed into the science of laws of composition defined for arbitrary sets of objects of arbitrary nature. From a modern viewpoint, the problem of solving equations in radicals is incomparably less important than the concepts of group and field it brought to life. But the theory of Diophantine equations retains its old significance (see [8] and [9]). In this century this theory has become amalgamated with algebraic geometry on the one hand and with number theory on the other, so that its role in the history of algebra is far from ended.

BIBLIOGRAPHY

1. Diophantus of Alexandria, *Opera omnia* (P. Tannery, editor), Vols. I, II, Teubner, Leipzig, 1893, 1895. (Greek; Latin prefaces)

2. ____, *Arithmetica* (translated by I. N. Veselovskiĭ; introduction and commentaries by I. G. Bashmakova), "Nauka", Moscow, 1974. (Russian)

3. H. G. Zeuthen, *Geschichte der Mathematik im 16. und 17. Jahrhundert*, Teubner, Leipzig, 1903.

4. I. G. Bashmakova and E. I. Slavutin, *History of Diophantine analysis (from Diophantus to Fermat)*, "Nauka", Moscow, 1984. (Russian)

5. François Viète, *Opera mathematica* (F. van Schooten, editor), Elzevir, Lugdunum Batavorum [Leiden], 1646; reprint (J. E. Hoffman, editor), Georg Olms Verlag, Hildersheim and New York, 1970.

6. R. Bombelli, *L'Algebra*, Giovanni Rossi, Bologna, 1572; reprint (edited and with notes by E. Bortolotti), Zanichelli, Bologna, 1929.

7. Evert M. Bruins, *Reciprocals and Pythagorean triads*, Physis **9** (1967), 373–392.

8. I. R. Shafarevich, *Basic algebraic geometry*, Springer-Verlag, 1977.

9. ____, *Zum 150. Geburtstag von Alfred Clebsch*, Math. Ann. **266** (1983), 135–140.

Moscow State University
   Moscow 117234
   USSR

Translated by A. SHENITZER with H. GRANT